SUSAN DiMOTTA
PERSONAL COPY

PICTURE
of HEALTH

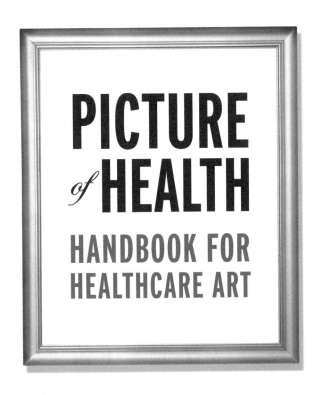

PICTURE
of HEALTH
HANDBOOK FOR
HEALTHCARE ART

by Henry Domke, M.D.

"We only see what we know."

—Johann Wolfgang von Goethe,
German writer, (1749–1832)

Published by Henry Domke Fine Art, 3914 Foxdale Road,
New Bloomfield, MO 65063.

For information about permission to reproduce selections
from this book, write to henry@henrydomke.com.

ISBN 978-0-9824651-0-3

Edited by Kim Reiss
Designed by Ana Rogers

FSC
Mixed Sources
Product group from well-managed
forests, controlled sources and
recycled wood or fiber
Cert no. SW-COC-001752
www.fsc.org
© 1996 Forest Stewardship Council

CONTENTS

INTRODUCTION

Let me share a true story with you.

A middle-age woman in a small Illinois town had cancer. Because of this, she had to make regular trips to the hospital for chemotherapy. A frightening ordeal—there's no way around it. In the treatment center waiting room, the woman noticed a large picture. It was a photograph of a big oak tree in a summer forest with morning sunlight streaming through the branches, illuminating the forest floor and its lush undergrowth.

She started coming in early for her appointments so she could look at the picture and meditate before going in for chemo. She even talked about it with her cancer nurse, saying that the way the sun shined through the trees, she almost "felt like God was going to walk out."

Whatever she saw there, it brought her a sense of peace and comfort during an incredibly stressful and frightening time in her life.

I don't know the woman's name, but I do know the picture: White-Oak_1055. The cancer center was at Blessing Hospital in Quincy, Ill., and I heard the story from the nurse.

That's why I'm writing this book. Not only for that cancer patient, but also for all the patients, family members, and staff in healthcare environments. As a doctor, I've spent a lot of time in hospitals, and I know what stressful places they can be. Even in the best of circumstances, such as having a baby, it can be a scary and anxious time. But when you're experiencing something truly life-threatening, being in a clinical environment can make you feel even worse.

What if, instead of that cold space, you could look at images that triggered thoughts of happy times in nature, scenes that transported you mentally to a better place?

SO WHY ME? WHY THIS BOOK?

This book is a collection of entries from HealthCareFineArt.com. I started the blog in March 2007 because I couldn't find the information I wanted anywhere else.

I'm not an expert, but I am an artist and a retired physician. And I'm a curious person—I want to know: How are people choosing art for hospitals? Is there "ideal" art for healthcare environments? Can some art actually be harmful? What can we do to ensure that art is included in building budgets? And on and on.

I started digging for information and talking to people. By putting my thoughts and findings on the web in a blog, I found many people had the same interests and questions. Research continues to be conducted, and awareness of the issue is growing. In that respect, I'm satisfied with what I set out to do—get people talking about art in healthcare, think about it in different ways, and possibly elevate its importance.

This book isn't intended to be the Last Word on art for healthcare. I really see it as a companion to the blog, which is ongoing. There you'll find more resources, interviews, featured artists, and other material that I simply didn't have room to include here. The book covers material posted to the blog through early 2009.

WAIT—AN ART BOOK WITH NO PICTURES?

If you visit the blog, you'll find pictures. Lots of pictures—good ones, bad ones, controversial art, uplifting images, and everything in between. Why write a book about art and not include any pictures? Several reasons.

The first is economic. To produce a proper picture book with color photographs was just too expensive. Second, I borrowed many images for the blog. It would be a legal and copyright nightmare to get all the permissions necessary for a book.

So the rebel in me said, "Let's do this art book with no pictures—and make it good!" My intention is to explore the ideas with words, interviews, quotes, and musings.

WHO MIGHT FIND THIS BOOK USEFUL?

There are a variety of people who might find the information in this book interesting, including art consultants, interior designers, architects, facility managers, and artists.

I hope it is used to generate discussion and trigger some creative thinking. How can we continue to study art and its impact on those who view it, especially the sick? How can we use art in new and existing facilities that have shrinking or even disappearing budgets? How will selecting art for healthcare evolve over the coming years?

You tell me . . .

ABOUT THE AUTHOR

I can't talk about the blog, my art, my business, or even my past medical practice without talking about the Prairie Garden Trust (www.prairiegardentrust.org). Most of the pictures I take are of the PGT, which is a 500-acre prairie restoration project in central Missouri. It's also where I live. My parents started the effort in the early 1970s with the goal of restoring native plant life to our little section of the world, and in doing so, restoring native animal life, as well.

So yes, I like nature. I like to take pictures of nature. How am I different from a "nature photographer?" For starters, I see myself as an artist first, and a photographer second. I also don't think you need a world-class botanical garden or the majesty of the Grand Canyon to capture beauty outside. My goal is to find beauty in the ordinary.

I continue to photograph the same ground, figuratively and literally, over and over. Because it's always changing—the light changes, leaves fall, dew forms—it's a new landscape every minute of the day, every day of the year.

In a serendipitous turn of events, it seems that photographs of nature seem to help sick people heal faster and feel better. So in that respect, I'm the luckiest man alive. I am able to combine so many of my passions—healing, art, nature, photography, and the Prairie Garden Trust—to hopefully make a difference in people's lives. And use income from it to keep this small part of the planet as a place where others can enjoy nature, too.

I invite readers to visit the blog if they haven't already. It's updated several times a week and seems to have developed a small following among those of us interested in this specialized niche. There's also a link to my email there, which is hands-down the best way to contact me with blog feedback, future posting ideas, and even thoughts about this book.

www.HealthCareFineArt.com

(Note: Blog posts and comments have been edited slightly for style and consistency. Typos and grammatical errors have been corrected, and some comments have been shortened or deleted because of space limitations, but every effort was made to keep each writer's text as authentic as possible. In addition, post entries in this book are not necessarily in chronological order.)

EVIDENCE-BASED DESIGN

IS THE MOST POPULAR ART THE BEST ART?

For healthcare, the short answer is YES.

Surveys have been conducted to find out what it is that people (regular people, not people who go to gallery openings), want in their art.

Artists Vitaly Komar and Alex Melamid carried out an interesting series of surveys in the 1990s to find out what it was that people really wanted. They published their results in an amusing art book, "Painting by Numbers: Komar and Melamid's Scientific Guide to Art." This book and their website depict the most and least popular art in different countries around the world.

What struck me was how similar their results are to what scientific studies have shown for healthcare. Roger Ulrich and Laura Gilpin summarize some key ideas on what art is best for healthcare in their book, "Putting Patients First."

Some of their top recommendations include art that depicts:

• Representational landscapes
• Calm water
• Calm weather
• Visual depth with openness in the immediate foreground
• Landscapes during the warmer seasons
• Landscapes with low hills and distant mountains

Their description of what is ideal for healthcare settings is virtually identical to the survey results of Komar and Melamid. What is ironic is that Komar and Melamid are Russian-born American conceptual artists. How odd that they would come up with the painting that is the exact representation of what research says is needed for healthcare.

COMMENTS

As a student of neuroscience, and one who has been studying the brain and the mind for the past 12 years, I think I can say the following:

Most of the "hardwired" networks in our brains were formed about 10,000 to 50,000 years ago. It takes that long for changes in the brain to pass through the evolutionary cycles that will permanently and universally implant them. During that time, we were living in primitive communities located on the savannas of the African plains. These savannas are characterized by an open meadow, perhaps with a stream of water running through the meadow, surrounded by a border of trees, and open sky. This gave our ancestors the comfort of feeling that any predators lurking in the trees would be seen if they ventured into the open meadow, giving our ancestors time to flee.

Today school children all across the United States, when presented with photographs of a variety of landscapes, indicate a preference for a landscape that resembles a savanna.

It should not surprise us to find that this painting is popular with most people.

Posted by: John Paul Eberhard | March 24, 2007 at 08:20 PM

Thanks for your blog and the great information you're offering daily.

I manage therapeutic arts and activities at an acute medical facility. For a couple of years we've had a selection of prints that we deliver to patients, offering an opportunity for people to make their own choices about what they look at when they are lying in their hospital beds. Most of the prints fit the criteria that you've described. I think the effectiveness of the program is due to both the kind of artwork available and the fact that people are invited and empowered to make choices at a time when they feel they have little control over their lives and environment. It's exciting to witness the healing benefits of the art!

A great resource with which many readers are probably familiar is the Society for the Arts in Healthcare (http://thesah.org).

Posted by: Alice Kinsler | March 26, 2007 at 10:02 AM

WHERE'S THE BEEF? THE EVIDENCE FOR EVIDENCE-BASED ART

What is the evidence base for evidence-based art? Where is rigorous evidence about the impact of art on key healthcare outcomes to be found?

The spring 2008 issue of Health Environments Research and Design has the answers. But I have to admit, it reminded me of the old ad, "Where's the Beef?" It turns out that there isn't much "beef" —or "evidence" yet. But there is some and more is being learned all the time.

What is known is summarized concisely in two paragraphs from the article in HERD titled, "A Review of the Research Literature on Evidence-Based Healthcare Design."

> Rigorous studies on hospital art are sparse, and most have measured patient art preferences rather than effects on outcomes such as pain. The limited findings nonetheless show similarities to results from nature studies. Results suggest a consistent pattern wherein the great majority of patients prefer and respond positively to representational nature art, but many react negatively to abstract art (Carpman & Grant, 1993; Ulrich, 1991; Ulrich & Gilpin, 2003). Nanda, Hathorn, and Neumann (2007) displayed a diverse collection of 17 paintings to patients in their hospital rooms, and asked them to rate each painting for the following questions: (1) How does the picture make you feel, and (2)

Would you like to hang this picture in your hospital room? Findings indicated that patients were significantly more positive about nature paintings (landscapes with verdant foliage, flowers, and water) than they were about best-selling pictures or even works by masters such as Chagall and Van Gogh (Nanda et al., 2007). The most positively rated painting depicted a gentle waterfall with vegetation. In the same research, representational nature paintings containing human figures and harmless animals such as deer were preferred over counterparts that were somewhat abstract. Eisen (2006) studied the art preferences of schoolchildren and hospitalized pediatric patients across four age groups: 5–7, 8–10, 11–13, and 14–17 years of age. Findings suggested that, irrespective of age or gender, the great majority of hospitalized pediatric patients and schoolchildren were similar in preferring nature art (such as a forest setting with lake and deer) over abstract or cartoon-like images.

Although nature pictures elicit positive reactions, there is limited evidence that emotionally inappropriate art subject matter or styles can increase stress and worsen other outcomes (Ulrich, 1991, 1999; Ulrich & Gilpin, 2003). It may be unreasonable to expect all art to be suitable for high-stress healthcare spaces, because art varies enormously in subject matter and style, and much art is emotionally challenging or provocative. The pitfalls of displaying emotionally challenging art are revealed by a study of psychiatric patients housed in a unit extensively furnished with a diverse collection of wall-mounted paintings and prints (Ulrich, 1991). Interviews with patients suggested strongly negative reactions to artworks that were ambiguous, surreal, or could be interpreted in multiple ways. The same patients, however, reported having positive feelings and associations with respect to nature artwork. Additional evidence on the stressful impact of abstract art comes from a study of a sculpture installation created for cancer patients in a large university hospital (Ulrich, 1999).

Prominent in the installation were several tall metal sculptures dominated by straight-edged and abstract forms, many having pointed or piercing features. A questionnaire study found that 22% of the patients reported having an overall negative emotional response to the sculpture garden (Hefferman, Morstatt, Saltzman & Strunc, 1995). Many found the sculpture ambiguous ("doesn't make any sense"), and some patients interpreted the sculptures as frightening and asked for a room change so they would not overlook the artworks (Ulrich, 1999).

Find more information at www.herdjournal.com.

ESSENTIAL NEW BOOK ON EVIDENCE-BASED DESIGN

I've just finished reading Jain Malkin's new book, "A Visual Reference for Evidence-Based Design."

This is a significant book that should be on the desk of everyone involved with healthcare design.

It describes in clear language how and why you should use evidence-based design. Malkin digs in deep and presents the research behind evidence-based design. Thankfully, she does this in a practical, non-threatening way. This is not a dry academic text, but a useful handbook, a reference you will want to use frequently when working on projects.

Even more important, since design is a visual process, the book is filled with hundreds of large, full-color pictures that illustrate what she is writing about. These are not just pretty pictures; they frequently have lines drawn to point out key design features.

Summary:
- Outstanding. A "must buy"
- The most important book available on evidence-based design

Pros:
- Clear, practical writing
- Visually rich

Cons:
- Not much about the use of art in healthcare (only two pages!)
- Expensive ($200)

Minor issues:
- I found the way that the illustrations were clustered after each chapter to be confusing. Why not put them in the body of the text?
- I disagree with her emphasis on infection control. It is important, but I think she over-emphasizes it. In her interview, she says, "Infection control is such a big issue today; it has to be the number one thing that architects and designers understand."
- Why isn't this book available on Amazon.com? The only way to purchase it now is through The Center for Health Design.

The May/June 2008 Healthcare Construction & Operations just arrived with a splashy front cover featuring the book. It also includes an interview with Malkin.

RULES FOR PICKING COLORS

When I was a kid back in the 50s, I remember all hospitals were painted green—hospital green. It was a muted green that could be called pistachio.

There must have been some theory that it was more restful for sick patients. There are a lot of theories like that, even today. Should we believe them?

No!

It turns out that scientific guidelines for picking colors to go in hospitals and clinics are bogus, at least if you believe researcher Ruth Brent Tofle. Dr. Tofle did a comprehensive review of the scientific literature and concluded:

Use of color in healthcare settings is not based on a significant evidence-based body of knowledge.

The report is called "Color in HealthCare Environments" (2004).

Her sponsor was the Coalition for Health Environments Research. Her findings were presented in an 89-page document, but I can save you the time reading this rather formal report by saying that there is no scientific evidence supporting one color over any other in health-care settings.

So what do you do if you don't have scientific evidence to support evidence-based design? That is called art.

Note: the Coalition for Health Environments Research is now part of The Center for Health Design.

COMMENTS

There was a theory that because green is the complementary color of blood red, that green would be better for staff. A big change is that hospitals realize they must be much more competitive/business savvy and cater to many more users than staff, such as patients, visitors/guests, etc.

Posted by: Ruth Brent Tofle | April 09, 2007 at 05:19 AM

NATURE VS. VIRTUAL

I sent a link to my blog to my friend Carol Davit. She responded:

> I think that what is perhaps superior to fine art in hospitals is access to views of the natural world from within hospitals (although this is often not possible, hence the value of fine art). When I had my c-section a year-and-a-half ago and was in the hospital for four days, I was fortunate enough to see the mountains out the window all day long—I know it helped.

I think she is right. It prompted me to go back and read the most famous research article ever published on art in healthcare. I went to a local library and, without a lot of effort, found the full report. It was only two pages long and not painful to read. It turns out that the research in this landmark study agrees with her.

"View through a Window May Influence Recovery from Surgery," By Roger S. Ulrich Science, 1984, Vol. 224, 420–421.

The title of the article tells the story. It was the view through the window that was studied in this article, not looking at fine art.

Researcher friends of mine tell me that it is a big deal to be published in the journal Science. Landing an article there lends great credibility to the findings. This single article published 23 years ago is the foundation for the entire field of evidence-based art in healthcare.

Some of the key findings on the 46 patients that were studied:

- Patients with window views of the trees spent less time in the hospital than those with views of the brick wall: 7.96 days compared with 8.70 days per patient.
- In days 2–5, patients with the tree view took fewer moderate and strong pain doses than the wall-view group did. On average, patients with the wall view took 6.13 doses of moderate or strong pain medication, compared to 2.70 doses for those with the window view.

In simpler words, patients who got to look out a window at nature went home about one day sooner and took about half as much pain medication.

Carol Davit is the editor of the Missouri Prairie Journal, published by the Missouri Prairie Foundation.

COMMENTS

Amazing that your topic today would be views of nature from hospital rooms! My husband had surgery on his ankle earlier today in a Florentine hospital. As we waited for him to be taken into surgery, we just stared out the window at a lovely purple flowering tree. It had a soothing effect on both of us . . .

Also, I remember several years ago when my mother was in a semi-coma in the intensive care unit at Barnes-Jewish Hospital. She was placed on the side where the rooms had no windows. After a week, her doctor decided to move her to the rooms that had windows and natural sunlight to try to wake her up. And she miraculously "woke up."

I agree that the best choice for hospital rooms would be windows with a view of nature. Next best choice would be beautiful nature photos—like yours, Henry, and mine! Our photos are like windows of the world. We bring nature into the hospital rooms with our colorful, realistic photos!

Posted by: Elaine Poggi | April 23, 2007 at 06:16 PM

RESEARCH: ST. LUKE'S ART CART

New research continues to support the idea that nature images are the "people's choice" in hospitals. Furthermore, patients appreciate the ability to pick the art that hangs on their walls.

In a previous post I discussed "artotheques" where patients can select the art that hangs in their rooms. St. Luke's in Houston has a similar program, which they call the "art cart."

Dr. Upali Nanda recently conducted some research on the art cart program. Some of her key findings were:

- The act of choosing paintings becomes a means for patients to interact with volunteers, thus providing social support.
- The ability to choose paintings can give patients a perceived sense of control.
- Patients tend to create narratives/stories around the pictures in their rooms, especially if the image contains characters or elements they can relate to.
- Landscapes, non-threatening animals, and flowers are the most popular.

Upali Nanda, Ph.D., is vice president and director of research at American Art Resources, a pioneer and leader in the field of therapeutic environments.

COMMENTS

Art can contribute to building sense of place also. If you feel familiar in a space with nature fine art, you have more sense of control also.

Anything that helps relieve the inherent stress of healthcare settings has great impact.

Posted by: Beth Worthington | April 26, 2007 at 04:23 PM

PICKING ART BY NUMBERS

I keep going back and re-reading chapter 7 of the book, "Putting Patients First," by Roger Ulrich and Laura Gilpin. There are a lot of gems buried in there. For example, on page 120, they write:

> The decisive criterion for healthcare art is whether it improves patient outcomes, not whether it receives praise from art critics and artists or approaches museum standards for quality.

What an ambitious goal that is! To have art be part of the healing process. They are not just talking good intentions here; they are talking about proving the healing with research, just like you would study the effect of a new drug or surgical procedure.

What a radical way to judge quality! They are proposing that the best criterion for picking art to go in hospitals is not the traditional way of relying on the taste of experts. Instead, they ask us to impartially look at research data. Let the numbers pick the art.

Chapter 7 then goes on to describe some of the general characteristics that go into healing art.

It is hard for me to accept this idea, picking art by numbers and formula, but I am letting it influence the art I am creating.

COMMENTS

Henry, I just finished reading this chapter upon your recommendation. I agree completely with what the authors are saying because of my experience of caring for my mother while she was in the hospital for almost three months. It is true that inappropriate art really can disturb not only patients, but also family members. I urge all people responsible for placing art in hospitals to read that chapter! Another quote is: "...The research discussed in this chapter implies that visual artwork in healthcare facilities is no mere luxury or unimportant embellishment. To the contrary, findings increasingly support the notion that the evidence-based selection of emotionally appropriate art contributes an important environmental dimension to patient care—one that lessens patient stress and improves other medical outcomes." This supports my idea that art can help even in hospitals in Third World countries as we discussed earlier on your blog!

Posted by: Elaine Poggi | August 03, 2007 at 08:40 AM

WHAT IS A PEBBLE PROJECT?

An interior designer was talking about one of her big projects. After her first few sentences, she paused, and in a lowered voice, said: "It's a Pebble Project..."

To find out more about what it means to be a Pebble Project, I asked Mark Goodman, vice president project development at The Center for Health Design, a few questions.

What is a Pebble Project?

The Pebble Project Partnership engages healthcare providers to push beyond the standard design status-quo, measure the results of their new design innovations and share their data with the industry at large. By doing so, the collective work creates a ripple effect, contributes to the body of evidence-based design knowledge and changes the experience of healthcare for the better.

Why would a hospital want to be part of a Pebble Project?

Healthcare providers and their design firms join Pebble because they see the value in measuring and documenting the impact of the built environment on healthcare outcomes, satisfaction, safety, and performance. They understand that by joining the Pebble Partnership, they gain access to not only incredible learning and high-level guidance, but also become interwoven into a community of peers that are applying an evidence-based design process to their work, and that as a Pebble, ultimately their own research can bring national visibility and open additional local opportunities.

What does it cost to participate in a Pebble Project?

A minimum three-year commitment is required at $30,000 per year for providers.

Are all Pebble Projects in the United States?

No, Pebble can be located anywhere. One of our newest Pebbles is the Vancouver Island Health Authority of British Columbia, Canada.

Has a Pebble Project ever been done studying the impact of art on healthcare?

Yes, several Pebbles have taken a look at studying the impact of art in healthcare settings, including the University of Texas M.D. Anderson Cancer Center and St. Luke's Episcopal Hospital in Houston, and Laguna Honda Hospital in San Francisco.

Is there anything else you would like to add?

Building a new healthcare setting requires major capital expenditure. When you are evaluating the financial viability of your project, please use an evidence-based design process as part of your risk-management strategy. If done right, the rewards for your organization and the patients served will be many and long-term.

More information about Pebble Projects can be found on-line at The Center for Health Design website, www.healthdesign.org.

TASTE IS NOT NEEDED TO PICK ART

Evidence-based art offers scientific guidelines for picking art to be used in healthcare settings.

Nowhere in those guidelines is "good taste" or "aesthetic judgment" suggested as a prerequisite for picking the art. Is taste not mentioned simply because it is hard to quantify? Science has a hard time dealing with things that can't be measured objectively.

Evidence-based art is by definition scientific. Since beauty cannot be measured objectively, does that mean it does not matter?

I hope not!

But sometimes I wonder if those who are hot on the evidence-based design bandwagon are so enthusiastic about their new methods that the guidelines become everything. Is it too old-fashioned to rely on an art consultant or interior designer who has an experienced eye?

Also, the amount of actual "hard data" for picking art is quite limited. Perhaps in a century or two we will have enough information to be more helpful, but I don't see how taste can ever be left out. In the meantime, I suggest learning what research has to offer, but seek out experienced art consultants or interior designers to help with the art selection process.

I asked Dr. Upali Nanda, who knows a lot about evidence-based art, to comment on this:

I believe the evidence-based approach is about 'informing' taste and aesthetic judgment, not 'replacing' it.

It makes the argument that in the context of healthcare where we deal with vulnerable populations, aesthetic judgment cannot be arrogant. Art, regardless of its aesthetic merit, cannot be imposed on patients if it has the potential to adversely impact their healing. In fact, given that art has the potential to heal (and here the evidence supports the impact of the visual image), it would be callous not to work towards that objective.

That said, neither the evidence, nor the approach, can replace expertise and sensitivity. The choice of art, the placement of art, the coordination of artwork with the overall design to create a cohesive and coherent environment, and so much more, is the task of an art consultant. One who can complexly process issues of color, balance, proportion, context, etc. to make a decision on what 'feels' right for a particular project.

All the evidence does is empower this decision process with a deeper understanding of human perception, and the impact of the components of the visual image on this perception, in the context of healthcare populations.

As a final note, I believe that your concern that evidence-based guidelines might come at the cost of the immeasurable aesthetic judgment (and as a researcher, I will add that it is immeasurable to date, but that might change too) is the main reason why PRACTITIONERS should invest in research. They are the ones who can ask the questions that get to the heart of the issue, and who can implement the answers without compromising on the immeasurable quality that is so essential to the design streams.

Upali Nanda, Ph.D., is vice president and director of research at American Art Resources.

BIOPHILIA—THE REASON NATURE ART HEALS

I've just learned a new word: biophilia. I came across it when I was going through a stack of old Contract magazines and found an article titled "Natural Needs" in the March 2007 issue. It was written by Sofia Galadza, director of public relations for IA Interior Architects.

Galadza defines biophilia as the study of a human's inherent tendency to affiliate with the natural environment. She says it could become the new buzzword in green design.

The term is not new; it was introduced and popularized by evolutionary biologist Edward O. Wilson in his book, "Biophilia," published in 1984. In the book, Wilson argues that humans have an innate and evolutionarily based affinity for nature.

Researcher and author Roger Ulrich makes an almost identical argument when he explains why nature art is good in healing environments in his book, "Putting Patients First."

Cultural explanations have proven inadequate, however, for explaining the mounting scientific evidence that a diversity of cultures and socioeconomic groups exhibits striking agreement in responding positively to nature views. Compared with cultural explanations, evolutionary theory readily accounts for this similarity by proposing that millions of years of evolution have left a genetic mark on modern humans in terms of a predisposition to respond positively to nature settings that fostered well-being and survival.

In other words, views of nature enhance healing because we are programmed genetically to respond positively to these views. Our positive response is one of reduced stress. It is the reduced stress that promotes healing.

THE REAL DRIVING FORCE BEHIND EVIDENCE-BASED DESIGN

The main pitch to sell evidence-based design is showing research that it helps patients. However, the main reason hospitals are willing to pay extra is not research, but consumer demand. It turns out that many of the design changes that EBD supports are perceived by patients as creature comforts. For example:

- Single-patient rooms
- Exposure to nature with pictures and gardens
- Extra space for family members
- Quiet rooms
- Natural light

Increasingly, patients not only expect these comforts, they demand them. If you don't have them, patients will go elsewhere, and that impacts to bottom line.

A recent article in San Diego's Union-Tribune by Keith Darce explores this idea. He talked about how EBD was used in the new 334-bed, acute-care tower at Memorial Hospital in Kearny Mesa, Calif. The article is titled, "At Region's New Hospital, Creature Comforts Count."

While studies indicate that some of the creature comforts help patients get well faster, consumer demand is the real driving force behind the trend, said Janna Binder of Professional Research Consultants, a company in Omaha that researches the healthcare market.

"Pretty soon it's going to be expected for a hospital to have high-definition screens (in patients' rooms) and gardens," she said.

TOP 10 WISH LIST FOR ART RESEARCH

Research into evidence-based art has given us a few guidelines on how to best select art for the healing environment, but there is a lot we don't know. Here are my suggestions for the 10 areas that would benefit from research:

- Does original fine art work better than poster art?
- Does the size of the artwork matter?
- How does black and white compare to color in effectiveness?
- Do images showing local habitat work better than exotic habitats?
- Do images of real (wild) nature work better than gardens or parks?
- Is the ideal art for use in public spaces of hospitals the same as or different than the art used in patient rooms?
- Is the art that is best for patients also the best for staff and family?
- Do prints on canvas (with no glazing) work better than prints on paper behind glass?
- Does art work illuminated with spots work better than art that just uses ambient light?
- Do patients who are connoisseurs of art have different needs? Are their responses to art similar to others when they are sick, or is it safe for them to have abstract art?

If you have any other suggestions for topics you would like to see researched, please email them to me or leave them as a comment.

DESIGNERS' PREFERENCES FOR ART MAY HURT PATIENTS

Today is the last day of the Healthcare Design 07 Conference.

I attended a talk that presented surprising new research news: interior designers' choices for art in healthcare can hurt patients.

The research was conducted by Dr. Upali Nanda of American Art Resources and Dr. Sarajane Eisen of Auburn University. They presented their findings in a talk titled, "Evidence-Based Art for Health-care and the Difference in how Patients and Design Students Select Artwork."

The take-home message that I got out of the research presentation was that interior designers should not be swayed by their personal preferences when selecting art for healthcare clients. Instead, they should select realistic nature images.

Here is why: Experienced art viewers—like interior designers—tend to prefer artwork that is challenging and emotionally provoca-tive. However, challenging artwork, such as abstract art, is not pre-ferred by many people, and in fact, can be very stressful and therefore harmful to patients.

Designers need to understand that research repeatedly shows that most people (i.e., not experienced art viewers) have a strong tendency to favor nature scenes.

Research also shows that nature scenes are ideal for healing environments because they can improve patient outcomes (evidence-based art).

COMMENTS

Your synthesis of the talk is right on mark—but I would suggest a couple of minor modifications:

1. The title—Designers' personal preferences for art CAN hurt patients. It's important to temper the title—many designers are empathetic, but need to be better informed.

2. "The take-home message that I got out of the research pre-sentation was that interior designers should not be swayed by their personal preferences when selecting art for healthcare clients. Instead, they should select realistic nature images."

I would change this last sentence: "Instead they should do some research, follow the evidence, and select what is appropriate for the healthcare client – such as realistic nature images."

You will be the first to agree that research needs to be interpreted carefully and stop short of being prescriptive. Even within nature images, elements such as depth of field, horizon lines, verdant foliage —and so much more—is critical. Not all realistic nature images are equally appropriate.

Posted by: Upali Nanda | November 08, 2007 at 07:00 AM

DOES EVIDENCE-BASED DESIGN MEAN PAINT BY NUMBER?

Enthusiasm for evidence-based design may have gone too far, and that might stifle creativity and lead to prescriptive design. At least that is what one designer said to me on the phone today.

Just because evidence-based design is a great idea (and it is!), that does not mean that we have all the evidence yet. In fact, the scientists doing this type of research tell me that less than 5 percent of design decisions have solid evidence behind them.

Designers may assume that just because a few studies have been done on a given topic that there is a "right answer" on how to do something and they should not question it; after all, it has science behind it. But the research may be flawed, or it might not apply to their given situation. Furthermore, some kinds of questions can't be answered with numbers, and therefore can't be reliably researched.

Until we have definitive evidence on a certain situation, what should we do? The designer I was speaking with (who shall go unnamed) suggests that designers consider evidence-based design as only one of many tools that can be used on a project. She urges:

- Using creativity to seek a "vision"
- Being aware of making decisions that are too safe
- Taking a more holistic view
- Considering meaning, considering the sacred
- Avoiding "painting by numbers"

COMMENTS

There is a lack of understanding of what "evidence-based design" is and its purpose. First, in the professional design world, we seek to find solid justifications that guide our decisions—thus, "evidence."

Otherwise there would not be any guidelines for decision makers, and design would not build upon what has already been done effectively and purposefully. Why would we as designers not want to be informed, and use this information to base our design decisions? We learn from those that went before and build upon that. Isn't it the same in medicine, making decisions based upon those that came before? And the research provides grounded evidence as to what works best.

We cannot design purely on intuition, without decisions grounded in informed knowledge, particularly when we are designing for a vulnerable population. Yes, there are so many unanswered questions — researchers in healthcare have just begun to tap into the most surface layer of interior environmental issues that affect patients, family, and staff. I find that those that question "evidence-based design decisions" are typically those who don't want their opinions challenged and don't really want to grow in knowledge, thus to become better in their given field.

Please do not quote me — but I enjoyed responding!
Posted by: anonymous | November 27, 2007 at 05:27 PM

EBD is not meant to be a roadmap. I'm in complete agreement that what we don't want to get to is a cookie-cutter approach to healthcare design, but to me, the evidence has only ever been a guideline that needs creativity added to it in order to create the appropriate solution for that client in that community.

We do have a long way to go in the area of research, and that to me is the exciting part. Every year it seems like we grow by light years in what we have learned, and yet we still have so much more to uncover and learn.
Posted by: Debra Levin, President and CEO, The Center for Health Design | November 28, 2007 at 05:06 AM

There is a general misunderstanding of how evidenced-based design might integrate with the architectural design process. There is not presently a "body" of knowledge from neuroscience that could be used for evidenced-based design. It will take 10 to 20 years for that to happen.

When it is large enough, this "body" of knowledge will be like the ones used for acoustical, lighting or structural design in present practice. I don't think architects feel constrained by having these engineering tools for designing, and they are not likely to be anymore constrained by evidenced-based design from neuroscience.

Posted by: John P. Eberhard | November 28, 2007 at 08:08 AM

EBD is hardly prescriptive—it is intended to spark innovation by building upon the foundation of known outcomes. If we do not measure and report our successes and failures, then we, like lemmings, follow the most current trend, which may be wrong. If all projects followed an evidence-based approach, then we would look to the existing body of knowledge, build upon it, hypothesize a new or different outcome, and then measure and report our findings for better or worse. It is here where we will advance the understanding of how to truly build healing environments. We have a long way to go, and need more designers willing to take this approach.

Posted by: Rosalyn Cama | November 28, 2007 at 08:51 AM

No science can claim to have all the evidence. EBD is at its early developing stage. That's exactly why more rigorous research is needed. However, we can do better if we make our decisions based on the available research evidence. We've already seen reports that EBD results in better outcomes. EBD has raised the bar for healthcare architecture. It challenges designers to be able to critically evaluate the evidence and creatively incorporate the evidence into design. At the same time, it provides new opportunities for artistic design

Posted by: Xiaobo Quan | November 28, 2007 at 09:19 AM

The term itself, "evidence-based design," reeks of hubris. It is not design based on evidence, it is design justified by subjective studies.

Posted by: Riprap | November 28, 2007 at 11:42 AM

First, I will preface by saying that healthcare has transformed in wonderful ways over the last 20 years, and I have high hopes for its future vision. I want to remind us that the education and training of architects and designers is one of problem solving . . . In my mind, EBD is a tool, and if understood as that, is another filter through which design energy can and should be channeled for best outcomes . . .
Posted by: barbara crisp | November 30, 2007 at 10:05 AM

From my view EBD, although a laudable concept, currently lacks the rigor to call itself a science. For example, consider the private patient room that incorporates same-handedness, electronic medication administration, and decentralized nurse work areas with electronic medical record access. If this room is considered a prototype for a safer room, should we incorporate all these principles in our future designs? Or have just one or two design aspects actually contributed heavily to a safer room and the rest of the design features are neutral in terms of safety?

I appreciate the desire of our healthcare design industry to become more disciplined in our understanding of the impact of our designed environments and EBD holds promise. In these early days, though, we should consider some of the EBD results more informational and anecdotal, rather than hard science.
Posted by: Jeni | November 30, 2007 at 11:54 AM

. . . I think that the framework of evidence-based design offers equally valid data. Remember, all studies do, for example in drug studies, is offer a statistical analysis of what happened when specific patient populations did specific things. And the exceptions outnumber the rule.

The cookie-cutter fear is a myth. There is no way, for example, one can write a healing song based on an analysis of a Mozart sonata. Only one Mozart and one may be enough . . .

The concern I have, however, is that EBD will provide a good excuse to do nothing . . . a way for a hospital to resist changes needed because the data has not yet been collected in the form that will push them into doing something (anything).

A great discussion!!
Posted by: Susan Mazer | July 01, 2008 at 07:56 PM

EVIDENCE-BASED DESIGN IN SWEDEN

Atenga is a Swedish firm promoting evidence-based design. I asked Atenga Morelli to tell me a little bit about her company.

Atenga Health by Design at first glance looks like an interior design firm, but in fact, it is much more, yes?

We are not an interior design firm. Our main activity is evidence-based research. We do design assessments, post-occupancy evaluations, observational studies, etc. We focus on the crossing point between design/architecture and human behavior/health in various healthcare environments.

Our aim is to raise the importance of the physical environment as a crucial part of the healing process by conducting good quality research and research-based consultations.

In addition, it's important to move this relatively young research field forward, and we like to contribute to this momentum. To achieve this, we cooperate with architects and interior designers, as well as all healthcare professionals.

On your website, you refer to "people-oriented design" and "the integration of human health factors into place making." Tell us more about that.

People-oriented design generally involves the study of how spaces best can serve human needs and desires (psychological, social, and behavioral). This includes all users of the space, be it patients, staff, or family members, etc.

The approach is often referred to as social design, pioneered by Robert Sommer. It emphasizes working with people rather than for them, to involve them in the process of planning and managing spaces. To inform them about the effect of humans on spaces and on how the built environment affects human health and well being.

Integrating human health factors into place making refers to creating settings that match the needs and activities of the users; to change health behavior, i.e., enhancing social interaction among institutionalized elderly, increase users' sense of personal control, facilitate wayfinding, thus lowering stress levels, and so on.

You have had several publications in the last few years. Are you actively involved with research at Atenga Health by Design?
Yes, this is the core activity of our operation. At the moment, I'm involved with a very interesting research study on multi-sensory environments in dementia care. We are investigating the use of a Snoezelen-type room (controlled multi-sensory stimulation) as an alternative to anti-anxiety or sedative medication for aging residents with agitated or aggressive behaviors.

I'm also planning a research study in the near future, an assessment of the integration of multi-sensory environments throughout dementia facilities and how this parallels organizational development.

Who are your clients?
Our clients are private practitioners, such as dental practices, who are interested in an environment that will reduce anxiety for patients. Other private practitioners include counselors, psychologists, and psychotherapists who want to create a safe and trusting setting for their specific clients.

Facilities for the aging are the biggest category of clients that contact us. In Sweden, most facilities are municipal, and the government has invested a considerable amount of funding for new facilities that are being planned and built at the moment.

The last category of clients is architecture and design firms that may need a specific research study, such as a post-occupancy evaluation, to improve the quality of their services.

Is art selection part of the service that you provide?
Yes it is, usually as part of our general consultation services. We do

not actually buy or frame the artwork, but often give suggestions of placement, material choice, and specific artist, image and color choice, etc. As an artist and art-therapist, I feel confident of my abilities to provide sound consultations in this area. And I firmly believe that visual art and other art forms such as music significantly contribute to supporting the health processes of the patient or viewer. There is so much interesting research on cultural activity and human health. This is an area I really want to explore further.

Is the idea of evidence-based design widely accepted in Sweden today?
It's a difficult question to answer. In one way I would say yes, because serious research and evidence-based research is a long-standing tradition, particularly in medicine in this country. At the same time, the interdisciplinary field of healthcare design/architecture to support health and human behavior is not as developed compared to the United States.

In my experience, it is elderly care that is pioneering the field in Sweden. There is a lot of interest among the general public. However, the field is not fully recognized by the establishment yet. Over here, these things take time. Having lived in Canada for 14 years, the experience can be rather frustrating at times!

Atenga Morelli lives and works in Stockholm, Sweden. For more information, go to www.atenga.net.

EVIDENCE-BASED ART IN IRELAND

I was surprised at the lack of discussion about evidence-based design at the symposium on "The Importance and Value of Art in Health Care" at the Museum of Modern Art last week. I had almost given up hope; however, the last few talks of the day finally touched on the subject.

The talk that I found the most interesting was by Irish artist Denis Roche. He described an ambitious project he is involved with called the Open Window Project. They are studying the psychological impact of art on leukemia patients who are confined to a single room for six weeks after bone marrow transplantation.

Being in a hospital is stressful for any patient, but for bone marrow transplant patients it is much worse. Due to risk of infection, they have to be almost totally isolated. The hope is that the art will reduce patients' stress by connecting them to the outside world with a virtual window.

The window is actually an LCD panel that is about 2.5' x 3.5.' Patients have a choice about what they look at.

This research is being done with very careful technique. It is a randomized prospective trial that will have studied 500 patients when it is complete in another couple years.

IS EVIDENCE-BASED DESIGN OVERSOLD?

It surprised me that Dr. Ruth Brent Tofle, department chair of architectural studies at the University of Missouri-Columbia, feels that "evidence-based design" is an oversold concept. While we were meeting in her office yesterday, she told me that too many designers are embracing it without realizing that this is such a new field with many unknowns. Much work remains to be done. She estimates that less than 1 percent of design decisions are based on solid evidence today.

Over time, of course, this will change. And there is no doubt that the idea of applying rigorous scientific studies to design questions can yield true benefit for patients and hospitals. However, just because it is a good idea does not mean that we have all the answers. It will be many decades before designers will have real evidence to support most of their decisions.

She thinks that too many people have jumped on the bandwagon, and that they too easily follow prescriptive designs when there is no research to support them.

She is also concerned by what she sees as a reluctance to publish "negative studies." By this, she means studies that tried to prove that a certain design improved the outcome, but the research showed that, in fact, it did not.

Lastly, she thinks that most designers don't understand the research process, and that "taking a weekend course won't fix that." Good research is expensive, time consuming, and very difficult. To conduct good research requires working with an expert team—a team that understands research methodology. That usually means working with an academic institution.

COMMENTS

I think Dr. Tofle makes some very good points. I believe evidence-based design IS oversold—more reason for people to invest in it "critically" rather than "blindly." I think learning how to identify sound evidence, and rigorous research, in order to inform design, is as critical as investing in new research to build upon the evidence-base. Finally, I could not agree more with the point that good research does need expert input in those trained in research—and this does make it expensive. That said, I think research "awareness" is something that we CAN work on—a weekend course can perhaps help designers understand what it is that research is all about, how they can be involved in collaborative projects to do research, and how good research can have a ripple effect on good design.

Incidentally, I agree with Dr. Tofle's points that there aren't enough negative studies out there. I think that the field is so new, and the faith in it so fragile, that there is a reluctance to test that faith. I suspect academic institutions will have to take the onus of being the impartial vendors of knowledge, because professional firms will always be a little hesitant to expose their failings (however well-meaning their intentions may be). But even if these failings are not shared as openly industry-wide as we would like, the firm internally does learn a lot from the process. In order to advance the industry as a whole, I believe partnering with academic institutions will be key—and will ensure that research is more than design justification.

Posted by: Upali Nanda | March 19, 2008 at 03:21 PM

Rather than being oversold, I think evidence-based design is not understood. It is a process, not a prescription. No one expects design professionals to become researchers, but rather be able to understand research and use it when they are designing healthcare facilities. This is the objective of The Center for Health Evidence-based Design Assessment and Certification (EDAC) program that is in its final stages of development. We decided to launch EDAC because we felt that people were jumping on the bandwagon without having a good understanding of what an evidence-based design process is. Hopefully, EDAC will help clarify that.

Posted by: Sara Marberry, EVP, The Center for Health Design | March 20, 2008 at 10:32 AM

Evidence-based design is well supported by academic and professional research. More and more practitioners are learning how to apply that research every day through the hard work of groups such as The Center for Health Design. As knowledge of evidence-based concepts becomes even more strongly rooted among design educators, a greater percentage of practicing professionals will have the sort of comprehensive knowledge needed to create great healthcare spaces. My work with practitioners and educators leads me to believe that healthcare environments that don't enhance patient experience will soon be hard to find.

Posted by: Sally Augustin, Ph.D., Editor, Research Design Connections | March 21, 2008 at 05:05 PM

FREE GUIDE TO EVIDENCE-BASED ART

The Center for Health Design just posted "A Guide to Evidence-Based Art" on-line. You can download the 23-page guide for free at www.healthdesign.org.

This is a must-read if you want to learn how evidence-based

design can help with art selection for hospitals. The paper was written by two experts: Kathy Hathorn, CEO of American Art Resources, and Upali Nanda, Ph.D., vice president and director of research at American Art Resources.

Here are some quotes:

- The physical environment is not a mere backdrop for healthcare delivery—it is an integral part of the hospital experience.
- . . . It is risky to place art in a hospital that is ambiguous, subject to interpretation, or that has obvious negative connotations.
- Carpman and Grant (1993) . . . concluded that patients preferred art depicting nature over scenes with urban content, pictures of people, architectural interiors, still-life, sport scenes, or abstractions.
- In another preference study, Eisen (2005) showed that children in hospital settings also preferred representational nature art to abstract art . . . contrary to common assumptions that children only like large cartoon-like or fantasy images . . .
- . . . Art programs focus on the more public areas of the hospital . . . patient rooms are more neglected . . . Yet, it is this wall that patients stare at endlessly while they are bedridden. This is why art carts, a service providing patients with a choice of art for their rooms, have gained popularity in recent years.
- Art has the ability to touch us deeply and profoundly in our most vulnerable moments. It serves as a focal point in the environment that we are confined in, which can offer an emotional escape. We are often quick to dismiss such a minute part of the environment, yet, when the patient scans around his or her surroundings, it is this focal point that often the eyes, and the mind, rest upon. It is up to us, as designers, to make this rest restorative.

EVIDENCE-BASED DESIGN: WHAT IS IT?

I just received my second copy of Health Environments Research and Design, the new journal on the use of research in design.

While skimming the table of contents, one article jumped out: "Evidence-Based Design: What Is It?" by Kirk Hamilton and Jaynelle Stichler, co-editors of HERD.

In my conversations with art consultants, designers, and architects, I get a sense that evidence-based design is a topic that generates a lot of confusion. To help clarify the confusion, I think this one page essay should be required reading. Here are some quotes:

> . . . there is also significant variation in how designers, and health-care clients define the term 'evidence-based' anything . . . These definitional variations can create unrealistic expectations about the process and skepticism about its efficacy in making a real difference in patient, provider, or organizational performance outcomes. The purpose of evidence-based design is to make use of data from multiple credible sources to guide design-related decisions with the ultimate goal of improving the patient care experience, the staff work environment, and organizational performance.

> Simply put, evidence-based design is the process of integrating the best research evidence, clinical and design experience, and client (patient, staff, hospital, and community) values to guide healthcare design decisions.

Incidentally, in the table of contents I did not see any topic specifically about the use of art in healthcare. But much of what is written there relates indirectly to evidence-based art.

COMMENTS

The question of what is "evidence-based" deserves much discussion centered around the larger question of "what is evidence." The current medical model goes back to the Pythagorean (Theorem) that says everything in the universe can be reduced to numbers. Following this declaration, eventually we came up with ways to do just that. However, the reality of the human condition is that most of what we are is not explained in digits. Rather the experience of being human is one that requires language, interpretation, description, and often dialogue to reveal what matters. It is "messy" to the scientist who would like to arrive at a statistical definition that would once and for all tell us all what to do.

The explanation of evidence-based design that Kirk and Jaynelle provided is broad and offers much depth in answering this question. Clearly, there is now a demand to use more than opinion and fad to serve the patient population and facilitate the work of hospitals. Nonetheless, given our current culture and addiction to science-by-numbers, we may still find the answers by trying to use methods that tell only one part of the story, ignoring the fact that within the unique experiences of patients and staff lie realities to which design can respond...We should all thank Kirk and Jaynelle for their vision and determination in bringing forward a part of the healthcare equation that has long been set aside for its refusal to easily be reduced to numbers.

Posted by: Susan Mazer | April 24, 2008 at 08:38 AM

REAL NATURE VS. PICTURES OF NATURE

Is experiencing nature through a plasma display picture of nature as good as looking at the real thing? Not according to some new research.

Many have assumed that photographs of nature would produce the healing results that Roger Ulrich first reported in 1984. That was the ground-breaking research article titled, "View through a Window May Influence Recovery from Surgery." The new study found just the opposite—that only views of real nature reduce stress.

The study measured individuals' heart recovery rate from minor stress when exposed to a natural scene through a window, the same scene shown on a high-definition plasma screen, or a blank wall. The heart rate of people who looked at the scene through the window dropped more quickly than the others. In fact, the high-definition plasma screen had no more effect than the blank wall.

Perhaps hospitals should be investing in more windows and landscape gardening than in art for the walls of their patient rooms.

One of the authors, Dr. Peter H. Kahn, reflects on what this might mean for our society:

> We are losing direct experiences with nature. Instead, more and more we're experiencing nature technologically through television and other media. Children grow up watching Discovery Channel and Animal Planet. That's probably better than nothing. But as a species we need interaction with actual nature for our physical and psychological well-being.

The article, "A Plasma Display Window? — The Shifting Baseline Problem in a Technologically Mediated Natural World," was published in the Journal of Environmental Psychology, Volume 28, Issue 2, (June 2008) Pages 192–199.

COMMENTS

Nice blog!

I also think it's a nice pairing of our current study with the 1984 Ulrich study that you highlight. I remember talking with Roger Ulrich at the 1992 Biophilia Hypothesis meeting (hosted by E. O. Wilson and Steve Kellert), and we and others there all pondered a little together about whether a real-time display of nature would garner similar psychological effects as actual nature. It took me a while to get the funding for the study!

Our lab also conducted a complementary study (which is also highlighted as a PDF on the homepage of our website). Abstract below.

In this study, we found physical, psychological, and social-organizational benefits for people who used a real-time plasma display window of nature in their inside offices for a period of six weeks.

Taking both studies together, here's our interpretation of this plasma window instantiation of "technological nature:" From the field study, we learn that when compared to experiencing no nature (as in an inside office), the plasma window of nature can provide important benefits. Thus when people must work in an inside office, such technological representations of nature are probably good things. But from our experimental study, we learn that when compared to actual nature, the plasma window of nature was not as good. This general pattern—that technological nature is better than no nature, but not as good as actual nature—is holding up across other forms of technological nature we've been investigating in our lab.

Thoughts?

Posted by: Peter Kahn | June 12, 2008 at 05:51 AM

I think your research is confirming some suspicions that many have had for a long time: there is no substitute for the real thing.

It is important to consider the implications of losing direct experiences with nature.

What is gained and lost as we become an increasingly urbanized world? Does it matter that fewer and fewer people ever experience true wilderness?

My wife believes that there are serious consequences for us and for the planet if we all end up spending our lives isolated from nature. She is trying to find ways to connect kids to nature again. Her inspiration comes from Richard Louv's book, "Last Child in the Woods."

Posted by: Henry Domke | June 14, 2008 at 10:05 AM

Henry and Peter, the studies are, indeed, informative and provocative. I say "provocative" because if the question is about static views of nature, clearly this opens the discussion of produced scenes of nature. In our production of the C.A.R.E. Channel, which has followed studies of Ulrich and others regarding the effect of imagery on patient outcomes, we have avoided static images and used, instead, a slowly produced series of images that avoids visual habituation and offers more variety and visual stimulation. At the same time, the

Discovery Channel production "Sunrise Earth" uses static imagery and the natural ambient sounds, and it is great for one hour and as pure ambience.

In my reading of the original study, I found it to be a stretch (regardless of the argument) that would point to digital media causing further detachment from nature that would lead to justified neglect of the earth. For those living in our most densely populated cities, nature is always artificial (as opposed to wild and random) and is overwhelmed by concrete. The stunning views of nature offered by photography and videography bring to the child and parent experiences otherwise inaccessible.

When a patient whose acuity level is high enough to deserve hospitalization is in need of stimulation that is restorative rather than agitating, nature imagery has been shown to be effective.

Perhaps the next study to do is one that really looks at the impact of broadcast media on the confined patient...

A great discussion to continue...

Posted by: Susan Mazer | June 30, 2008 at 10:13 PM

Susan, I say "provocative" because if the question is about static views of nature, clearly this opens the discussion of produced scenes of nature.

I dug in deeper by reading Dr. Kahn's article. His work is NOT using static images. Here's a quote on his methodology: "...a plasma window that afforded a real-time HDTV view of essentially the same scene..."

I will forward your comment to Dr. Kahn to see if he would like to comment.

Posted by: Henry Domke | July 01, 2008 at 05:50 AM

Henry, the HDTV literally looked out on the courtyard of the university... which was the look outside of the real window. So while the image was not fully non-changing, on a macro level, it was static. Some cruise ships have cameras on the helm which become a channel on the television . . . it was very boring . . . meaning, it did not do the job. I would say this was an upgraded equivalent.

I would define non-static imagery as one that moves through a variety of related images . . . not unlike how we all might glance into a park moving from object to object, view to view.

A different study is called for? Maybe for my dissertation?

Posted by: Susan Mazer | July 01, 2008 at 07:39 PM

NEW DEFINITION OF EVIDENCE-BASED DESIGN

The Center for Health Design just redefined evidence-based design:

> Evidence-based design is the process of basing decisions about the built environment on credible research to achieve the best possible outcomes.

I suppose if you wanted to define evidence-based art (which is just a form of evidence-based design), you might say:

> Evidence-based art is the process of basing decisions about art for healthcare on credible research to achieve the best possible outcomes.

EVIDENCE-BASED DESIGN UNDER ATTACK (PART 1)

World Health Design's premiere issue (April 2008) has an article introduced by Dr. Jacqueline Vischer, professor of design at the University of Montréal, comparing evidence-based design to research-based design. Because selecting art for healthcare is increasingly based on evidence-based design, I wanted to know more.

Dr. Vischer writes:

> The dark side of EBD is that time and other practical limitations might have ethical implications, leading to a compromise of research protocol or erroneous methods of data collection and analysis.

. . . It is important, therefore, not to substitute it for conventional research.

After reading the article, I could not understand how evidence-based design differs from conventional research (also known as research-based design). Because I was unable to reach Dr. Vischer, I asked an EBD researcher to comment.

Dr. Xiaobo Quan, a researcher at The Center for Health Design, writes:

> The discussion around EBD has revealed again that different people may have different definitions and opinions about the same term or concept. In my personal opinion, these are the same thing. EBD is research based.

COMMENTS

It is not designed to be a rigorous appraisal of evidence-based design, but simply to re-establish, using journalistic techniques, the debate on the true definition of EBD, which is a methodology that has been perverted by so many in the name of marketing.

The feature achieves its aim by exposing, as Dr. Xiaobo Quan recognizes, that many people have different definitions or even misconceptions about what constitutes evidence-based design.

In reality, this is the unfortunate consequence of many practitioners misusing and undermining the concept, by claiming a project to be evidence-based despite a less than rigorous research methodology.

Posted by: Marc Sansom | August 28, 2008 at 06:48 AM

What everyone seems to be forgetting is that evidence-based design is a process and is about both research AND design. It includes using the best available research, putting together the right team to make decisions based on that research, and using conventional research methods to measure results. The Center for Health Design and a group of industry experts have spent the past three years defining this process, which is the basis for its Evidence-based Design Accreditation and Certification (EDAC) program. The EDAC Study Guides, which are coming out this November, will clearly define this process. In addition, several really good books on EBD have been or are about to be published by experts such as Jain Malkin, Kirk Hamilton, and Roz Cama. The field is truly growing and it is good that we are having such robust discussions!

Posted by: Sara Marberry | August 29, 2008 at 09:29 AM

EVIDENCE-BASED DESIGN UNDER ATTACK (PART 2)

Previously I had written about an article in World Health Design that took a critical look at evidence-based design. I had been unable to reach the author, Dr. Jacqueline Vischer, a professor of design at the University of Montréal, before putting up that post. Now she has responded to a series of questions.

Note: in this interview, evidence-based design is abbreviated as EBD, research-based design is RBD, and post-occupancy evaluation is POE.

I'm not really clear on how EBD and RBD design are different. They both involve using scientific methods to test a hypothesis about a design process that might measurably improve patient outcomes, right? How do they differ? Cyndi McCullough wrote that "EBD is rooted more in healthcare provider observation and anecdotal evidence," while "RBD is more rigorous and is based on studies using comparative research instruments..." Is that true?

I do not distinguish between research-based design and evidence-based design; it seems to me that the terms could be interchangeable. EBD is gaining currency as a defined and specific approach whereby social science measurement tools are applied in a field situation to generate 'proof' that one design action or another is likely to be a more effective design solution, in terms of adding value to the designed outcome. Value that is added is usually in terms of beneficial effects on users, but users are a large and diverse group (staff, visitors, cleaners, the public . . .) and not limited to healthcare environments. I think the issue facing EBD—as I have written—is what constitutes 'evidence,' as most data analysis and testing is based on the statistical probability of one or another outcome being the result of something other than chance. The designer, as the participant who transposes the 'evidence' into a concrete act, still has the job of interpreting the results.

Research-based design seems to me at this point to be a slightly vaguer term, in that 'research' can include just about any activity that the designer opts to engage in as part of their problem analysis. My students use 'research' to describe looking up design solutions in magazines, studying the designs of published architects, reading articles and books related to the topic and or to the design process, as well as going into the field and questioning (systematically or otherwise) stakeholders. In reference to your question, I do not use either EBD or RBD to indicate a 'design process'—that for me is another term with a whole other meaning, or set of meanings. I also do not consider that either term is limited to healthcare environments, although this is where EBD is gaining currency at the present time.

Are you saying that EBD is fast and practical and that RBD isn't? If so, why?
No, I do not think 'fast' and 'practical' characterize either EBD or RBD. I wrote that the temptation to do research 'fast' can lead to dangerous waters both in terms of validity, that is, what exactly we think we are measuring, as well as reliability—that is, the effectiveness of the testing or measuring we decide to use. For me the appeal of EBD is the logical and practical link into design decision making, such that spaces designed for specific uses are based on what is known about user behavior rather than on the designer's speculation or limited personal experience. We used to think we could fix this problem with POE but we were not always effective. I think EBD is

a better way of improving the situation, but realistically it is not possible to perform research projects on every aspect of a design project. And anyway, why would one want to? Part of what the client is paying the designer for is his or her creativity, imagination, and intuitive problem-solving skills.

What are the "ethical implications" you are referring to when discussing the dark side of EBD? Are you are saying that EBD is more prone to rush research, which is inherently a time consuming process?

Yes, in part. I am also saying that there is a risk that a designer not trained in research can set up a bogus project in the name of EBD and then claim scientific validity for his or her design decisions. Most clients are not researchers, either, so are not in a position to distinguish between a piece of solid research and one that has taken shortcuts and led to biased results. You know the old saying: 'There are lies, damned lies, and statistics.' And we definitely live in a culture that values quantitative reasoning, regardless of what it is based on!

You mention the value of post occupancy evaluation. Can't POE be used in both EBD and RBD?

I would say that RBD, as an umbrella concept, can include POE as one way of doing research for design.

In my article I distinguish between POE and EBD, but I could well see how an EBD research project might be incorporated into a broad-based POE.

You did not mention the fact that EBD is in its infancy and the actual amount of hard data to guide designers of hospitals is remarkably small. Isn't that a serious concern for EBD and RBD?

The data that guides doctors in their medical decisions is also often 'remarkably small.' There is no objective standard of when we have enough data to make the 'right' decision. In that way, designers are no different from doctors. I stress the importance of the designer's experience, intuition, sensitivity, and principles—as well as research results in solving design problems. We do not want to find ourselves supporting a 'scientific' approach to design at the expense of all those other important factors; we may end up with a lot of bad designs!

Where does the title of your article, "The Methods of Our Madness," come from?
From the editor, I'm afraid!

COMMENTS

Thank you for your follow-up with Dr. Vischer. Her comments are both refreshing and rooted, and provide an excellent insight into the current Research Rush.

In fact, I wish there had been more of her perspective, and a discussion, in the article — it would have been of value to readers and prevented the label-dilemma of EB vs. RB; a spurious distinction at best given the infancy of fields and the confusion regarding definitions.

I particularly appreciate Dr. Vischer's cautionary note on bogus research — perhaps one of the biggest threats in the industry today.
Posted by: Upali Nanda | September 04, 2008 at 04:43 PM

A friend emailed me questioning Dr. Vischer's statement that "The data that guides doctors in their medical decisions is also often 'remarkably small.'"

Yes, I suspect that there is more hard "evidence" for physicians than there currently is for designers, but not as much as you would like to think. As a licensed physician, I would have to say that the vast majority of what is practiced as medicine today is based on expert opinion rather than hard science.

Let me make a guess: 10 percent of medical decisions are based on solid evidence. If the amount of solid evidence for design is 2 percent (my guess), then, yes, medicine is way ahead, but still has a long way to go.
Posted by: Henry Domke | September 09, 2008 at 10:23 AM

EVIDENCE-BASED DESIGN: PROS AND CONS

Dr. Anjali Joseph recently wrote a helpful post on The Center for Health Design's blog. She explores some of the current controversies around evidence-based design. Since many experts feel that EBD should be applied to the use of art in healthcare, I thought it would be useful to try to summarize the ideas:

Con: EBD is old hat.
Pro: EBD formalizes that old hat.

Con: EBD is cookbook design.
Pro: EBD is only one part of the process.

Con: EBD is the mindless application of research.
Pro: EBD looks to see if existing research applies to your project.

Con: High-quality research does not exist to answer most design questions.
Pro: It is true that EBD is in its infancy, but that does not mean it is wrong.

Con: It is hard to find what research has been done.
Pro: Use a resource librarian.

WHY THE WORD "GICLÉE" BUGS ME

Call me crazy, but the word giclée drives me nuts. I think it sounds pretentious. It sounds French. People always struggle to pronounce it correctly.

In fact, it is an invented term for the process of making fine art prints from a digital source using inkjet printing. The person that invented the word is not even French, he's American and his name is Jack Duganne.

What triggered this rant? I was reading the cover article "The Art of Healing" in the March issue of Healthcare Design. The article was written by Diana Spellman, president of interior designers Spellman Brady & Company in St. Louis. She makes several excellent points about why inkjet prints are now "state of the art" in healthcare facilities:

> Giclée prints connote an elevation in printmaking technology. Images are generated from high-resolution digital scans and printed with archival quality inks onto various substrates, including canvas, fine art and photo-base paper. The giclée printing process provides better color accuracy than other means of reproduction. I believe in using graphic images in larger-than-life-size to draw the person into the image. The quality of the giclée print rivals the traditional silver-halide and gelatin processes and is commonly found in museums, art galleries and photographic galleries.

Her ideas are correct and useful. If only she had used the word inkjet instead of giclée. This is not her fault or the editors' fault; they did not make up this phony word. But even though the word giclée is now widely used, it always makes me cringe. In case you want to know, the preferred way to pronounce it is "zhee-clay."

WHO SHOULD PICK HEALTHCARE ART?

Here is an idea that is hard to swallow: People who are highly trained in art probably should not be picking art for patients. For someone that has gone through art school and who is passionate about contemporary art, this is not an easy idea to accept.

Experts should pick the art! Connoisseurs, collectors, curators, and artists have well-trained eyes and a well-developed sense of taste. However, art has to be seen as a functional tool in the healing environment. It should be judged by how patients, patients' families, and staff respond. Not only does it contribute to healing, but it contributes to the bottom line by helping create satisfied customers and staff. Quoting Roger Ulrich from "Putting Patients First":

> . . . many artists and designers enjoy . . . art styles and subject matter that evoke negative reactions in most of the public. This implies that if artists and designers follow their personal aesthetic tastes and knowledge when selecting art for healthcare settings and fail to involve patient representatives or consult research evidence, they may unwittingly specify art that widely misses the mark of patient preferences and therefore provoke negative reactions.

The ideal person to pick art for healthcare settings is an art consultant or interior designer who understands the research on healing environments and patient preferences.

ABSTRACT ART CAN HURT PATIENTS

Gerhard Richter is my favorite living artist. But could his paintings, which are often abstract, be the worst possible art for a healthcare setting?

Roger Ulrich is the pioneering researcher on the use of art in hospitals. He might argue something like this:

Being a patient is a very negative and frightening experience. Abstract art, being ambiguous, is open to interpretation. If one feels bad, the interpretation is likely to be frightening; this is likely to trigger negative feelings. Those negative feelings could harm the patient. Furthermore, the majority of the public does not like abstract art.

This appears to be true in every country where it has been researched. The response to abstract art can even turn violent. Ulrich reports that in Sweden, there were seven incidents of patients actually physically attacking and damaging abstract works of art. It is clear that scores of research articles would say that abstract art is wrong in patient rooms.

Does this apply also to public spaces in hospitals? According to Kathy Hathorn, president and principal-in-charge of American Art Resources, "Regardless of its interest or critical importance, abstract art in a hospital lobby is clinically inappropriate."

There is one more reason why Gerhard Richter's paintings would not work well in most hospitals—budget. Richter's paintings routinely sell at auction for more than $1 million.

COMMENTS

Ouch! The global statements above are dangerously inaccurate. Contrary to the quotes you have used, my extensive experience proves the opposite. As in any public setting, consideration must be paid to the emotions evoked by any work of art. In abstract art the predominant factor is color. Using Richter's painting is a dramatic example of a painting that evokes despair by color and texture. There are a thousand (at least) other examples of abstract paintings that are uplifting. My current project involves 14 paintings for a medical facility, all abstract. Past healthcare projects have all included abstract paintings with great success. As just one example, my new series, Generations, has been very favorably received by the healthcare industry. http://www.art-girls.com/Decorative/generations.html
Posted by: Robin Walker | March 25, 2007 at 07:54 AM

Robin, thanks for your response. I hope I am wrong in my statement that abstract art is always wrong. I hope I am wrong because I love abstract art. But if we are going to follow the current guidelines of "evidence-based design," then clearly abstract art is wrong.

By the way, Robin, I love your paintings!

Posted by: Henry Domke | March 25, 2007 at 08:08 AM

I'd just like to add my voice to those dissenting against the idea that abstract art is problematic. I saw Dr. Ulrich present his paper on abstract art — I would be the first to say that he has done a lot for bringing people's attention to the healthcare environment, but have to point out that his definition of abstract art was — as I remember it — his and a colleagues' mucking about on Photoshop. Not exactly Richter. I've seen, and installed, some fantastic abstract work in hospitals. Art doesn't have to be a view to help people. The mind can escape through more windows than that.

Posted by: Victoria Hume | May 28, 2008 at 03:41 PM

I'm certainly not an art expert, but I am responsible for art selection at our hospital. I don't think there is any one simple answer to this question — each setting and piece of art would need to be evaluated individually. I think the main thing is to not put art that could seem disorienting in a setting where the patient is already emotionally or physically disoriented. I don't think that would be the case with colorful, cheerful or peaceful abstract art, but there are certainly some pieces — abstract or not — that evoke sadness, fear, or disorientation. I think those should be avoided.

Posted by: Michelle Rumbaut | July 19, 2008 at 09:32 PM

I think that everyone reading this needs no convincing of the power of art to stir emotion, promote wellness or speed up healing; and I imagine that we all know the old rule of thumb about using art that employs red sparingly because of its effect on blood pressure and ability to stimulate and excite. Research proves the theory and I imagine that there are volumes of research yet to be carried out and taken down on what styles of art should be used to good use in healthcare. I have never heard the rule of not using abstract art in the field and only recently said to a client how wonderful the Mayo Clinic and Brigham Young projects look to me. I think that this guideline to avoid abstraction is way too broad, general, and I'm dying to read the bottom-line research. I can tell you from my interest in art crime that way more frescoes and classical statues have been damaged and destroyed by protestors and lunatics of many sorts than the handful of Swedish cases mentioned above.

Also, there are just so many other factors to be taken into account —region, climate, architecture and the kinds of patients who use the facility are just a few that need to be taken into the process of choice.

Lastly, as much as I like Richter's work, this is a poor example to use. It is intense, moody, and I could see the recovering being annoyed with it just because there is so little about it that calms, inspires, or distracts. I know that calm water, landscapes, and pleasing palettes go a long way, but I am going to need a lot more convincing before I cease to pitch abstracts to healthcare.

Posted by: Antonio Arch | August 24, 2008 at 08:56 PM

That's just shit. It depends on the piece, obviously, and the patient's perspective on the piece. Generalizing all abstract as "dark" is a poor stereotype.

Posted by: Emma | September 14, 2008 at 11:58 AM

Emma, I agree it depends on the piece; and yes, I was generalizing to make a point. However, I suspect that the experts on evidence-based design would agree that abstract art is always wrong.

Posted by: Henry Domke | September 14, 2008 at 12:03 PM

CAN ABSTRACT ART PUT PATIENTS AT EASE?

Eleven large abstract paintings were recently installed at Truman Medical Center in Kansas City. Each painting is about 5 feet square and is done in primary colors. Caleb Fey, the new art curator at the hospital, described the works in a recent newspaper article:

> When I view the artworks, there's the chaos of the abstract but the rigidness of geometric forms that make sense of the chaos and brings it into focus. That's what patients go through when they're going through an illness.
>
> For me, it's all about creating a visual atmosphere for the patients that puts them at ease. This reduces stress, anxiety, blood pressure, all things that affect a patient's outcome. I believe they'll get well quicker if they feel at ease.

Saying he wants to "put patients at ease" sounds like the same language used by the proponents of evidence-based art. However, in reviewing the research, it would be fair to ask, "Can abstract art put patients at ease?"

Paraphrasing evidence-based art researcher Roger Ulrich:

> Being a patient is a very negative and frightening experience. Abstract art, being ambiguous, is open to interpretation. If one feels bad, the interpretation is likely to be frightening, which is likely to trigger negative feelings. Those negative feelings could harm the patient.

COMMENTS

My opinion, based on my personal experience in hospitals and my research of art in hospitals, is that "Cape Boyador" would not put me at ease. It would confuse me and create a very negative feeling inside of me.

Posted by: Elaine Poggi | February 11, 2009 at 04:09 AM

I looked at the image of the "Cape Boyador" with a patient's eye. I imagined sitting in a waiting room for an appointment, looking at this image and what it might "say" to me. I agree with the artist's assessment of chaotic, but I don't find anything soothing in the geometric form to counter balance the chaos.

The image seems "broken," in need of repair. Yes, a patient might feel that way if they're waiting for an uncertain diagnosis, but is reminding the patient of chaotic feelings helpful or healing? I would look for some image that expresses hope and wholeness . . . images of nature can take a patient out of the clinical environment. The images are so very familiar, and yet there is something magical, even mystical, about nature. The potential of new growth and the cyclical pattern of renewal and sustainability is reassuring and comforting.

Regards, Anne Schallhorn Parker, manager, interior design, University of Michigan Hospitals & Health Centers
Posted by: Anne Schallhorn Parker | February 11, 2009 at 10:10 AM

Providing a variety of art styles and mediums to meet the needs of a broad population is a philosophy I believe to be the most effective.

While "Cape Boyador" does not particularly resonate with me, there may be others who are reminded of places or events in their lives who would find it appealing.

Christine Guzzo Vickery, associate vice president, interior design, HGA Architects and Engineers
Posted by: Christine Guzzo Vickery | February 12, 2009 at 09:02 AM

I looked at "Cape Boyador" and it made me nervous—I can imagine someone who is ill would find it even more unsettling. Most articles I've read on the impact of art state that abstract art is just too ambiguous and difficult to appreciate for patients who are under stress. Softer, more literal images, whether people or nature, seem to be easier to relate to. That's my 2 cents.

Jeni Wright, principal, Kahler Slater
Posted by: Jeni Wright, AIA, LEED-AP | February 16, 2009 at 03:59 PM

"One shared interest—two different audiences." In viewing this artwork, I believe that there is "one shared interest," but perhaps two different audiences. Although the art that graces the general public spaces can be quite dynamic, simply due to location and size of the space, consideration still needs to be given to the content and message it may convey.

With reference to "Cape Boyador," if the artwork appears to depict chaos, why would they want to reinforce it on a large scale in their healthcare facility? Probably because it is on "loan" from a noted artist and raises "visibility" of the Truman Medical Center —also a very important factor in these economic times.

Perhaps we need to step back and realize that "one size does not fit all" when creating a healing environment—it will be unique to each hospital and its location . . . to have vision for the future we need to be cognizant of the many facets needed to create a healing environment. And although we are most concerned with patients' environment—we also need to realize the importance of a hospital's visibility when trying to vie for community support and/or donor funding, which really then becomes "one shared interest."

Dianne Stitzlein, DesignStudioOne.inc

Posted by: Dianne Stitzlein | February 21, 2009 at 02:42 PM

It is not well understood how people react to different types of abstract art. It can be disturbing if the person is upset, but a lack of diversity in the work, i.e., nothing but pretty landscapes, tends to get tedious. The response to my abstract image of primary colors that was purchased by Boone Hospital has had nothing but positive commentary and is hung in an area that will be seen by many people. It is also very different from most of the other art hung in the new wing of the hospital. Henry, it always seems like you're looking for an all or nothing kind of answer. With new art, it is always a very protracted period before the culture changes to grasp and understand what an artist has done. The overwhelming percentage of the population understands and loves impressionism, and as a culture, that is what we like. I think most of the population is still clueless about what Pollock did and why it is important.

Posted by: Peter Anger | February 22, 2009 at 03:15 PM

AVOID BLACK-AND-WHITE PHOTOS

Black-and-white photographs should be avoided in hospitals and medical offices. The general public dislikes abstract art, and research proves that it is inappropriate for healthcare. Since black and white is more "abstract," and since the general public prefers color, it is best to skip these prints.

I say that, of course, to be provocative. I love black-and-white photography; I grew up with it. My early work was black and white, which I processed myself and printed in the darkroom. Even today I have a gallery of black-and-white images on my website. The long tradition of art photography has been black and white. Even today, many connoisseurs prefer it.

One of my favorite photography magazines is LensWork. It prints only black-and-white images. LensWork's pages show rich images with deep blacks and subtle tonalities that almost glow.

COMMENTS

Speaking as a photographer who has spent a lifetime shooting black-and-white photographs and being calmed and soothed (and probably healed on some level) by the black-and-white work of other photographers, I have to respectfully suggest that you, Henry, have overstated your position. Color can actually be a distraction and add what I think can be a negative effect to either a beautiful moment or a breathtaking quality of light. Imagine some greenish fog in whatever beautiful place you love. I can't argue with serious research, but there are so many variables. You need to take another look at Eugene Smith's "Dream Street" or Edward Weston's shells and peppers. I'm hyperventilating a little just mentioning them.

Posted by: Nick Kelsh | May 19, 2007 at 03:36 PM

PATIENTS LOOK AT TV, NOT ART

In my experience, when I walk into patients' rooms, most of the time a TV is turned on. Often there is a news story about a war or some other disaster. Perhaps looking at the latest bad news is not conducive to a healing environment. What is a good alternative?

According to designer Jain Malkin, who wrote in Sara Marberry's book, "Improving Healthcare with Better Building Design:"

> An optimal solution for enabling patients to connect with nature in their rooms is by way of a large flat-screen TV and programs such as the Continuous Ambient Relaxation Environment (CARE) Channel. A disc with 60-hours of nonrepetitive nature images, accompanied by specially composed music based on research as to what is soothing or healing, is provided on a closed-circuit channel through the hospital's network. It can be set as the default whenever someone turns on the TV.
>
> A patient may select a specific nature image that will personally be the most healing and actually keep it on the screen as a piece of artwork as long as desired or allow the images to sequence.
>
> This system was developed for hospitals to provide an alternative to the noise of monitors and conversations overheard from nurse's stations. Built in is a 24-hour clock that adjusts the tempo of the music for nighttime vigils in the intensive care unit, for example, when TV with its annoying advertisements can be stressful for families.

For more information on the Continuous Ambient Relaxation Environment Channel, go to www.healinghealth.com.

COMMENTS

It is clear that the use of media in healthcare settings has not been handled with due care. Distraction theory says that pain can be mitigated by a distraction that has more "attraction" than the pain. Depending on the patient's level of acuity, a distraction that would work may include movies, television, the C.A.R.E. Channel, a family member visiting, a card game, or anything that would take his or her mind away from the physical pain. A separate issue is the insidious ways in which commercial television impinges on the therapeutic experience of patients, the anxiety and concerns of family members and visitors, and on the ability of the nurses, physicians, and other therapists to be fully present in their delivery of care.

To date, hospitals have held that they must provide a television —that variety of programming is imperative for patient satisfaction, that an entertained patient requires less attention, and that the television can successfully deliver patient education. For the many hospitals that now have the C.A.R.E. Channel, the television also is an environmental tool. Nonetheless, current commercial television programming offers the best and worst in regard to what will help a patient deal with the many hours during an admission and equally, what will contribute to anxiety and stress. I have a short article written after 9/11 regarding patient television that brings poignancy to this issue. (http://www.healinghealth.com/c-news/attacks.php)
Posted by: Susan Mazer | June 03, 2007 at 01:39 PM

KITSCH CAN WORK

Kitsch is a snooty word. Calling something kitsch is a way of looking down your nose at something, to say it is in bad taste.

The opposite of kitsch is avant-garde. Avant-garde means pushing the boundaries of what is accepted, to experiment and find something new. Avant-garde is cool. As we have discussed in previous posts, this kind of challenging art does not usually work in hospitals.

Can kitsch work in healthcare?

I think it can, if done thoughtfully. Kitsch relies on repeating a convention or formula. Much nature photography follows a formula. If one followed the "formula" for healthcare art outlined in chapter 7 of "Putting Patients First," the results would probably be fine.

Many artists would say that Thomas Kinkade is the most famous living painter producing kitsch. If kitsch means commercially produced items that are overused and lacking in originality, then yes, his work probably is kitsch.

Would his work be appropriate in a healthcare setting? If you read the specific suggestions of the experts, I would argue that his work would be perfect. He creates non-threatening romantic landscapes that are easily appreciated by the general population.

Hopefully the ideal art for healthcare would be something in between kitsch and avant-garde. Something conventional, but fresh. Something that evidence-based research supports, but also something that is new.

But please, no big-eyed paintings...

Incidentally, Susan Orlean wrote a wonderful article for The New Yorker about Thomas Kinkade called "Art for Everybody." I highly recommend it.

LIMITED EDITIONS – NO LONGER RELEVANT?

Limited editions are designed as a marketing tool. In most cases, its use is artificial.

The use of the term "limited editions" for photographic prints bothers me just like the pretentious fake word "giclée."

The idea behind limited editions is based on something real; it goes back to 19th century printmaking. Back then, many traditional printmaking techniques could only produce a limited number of top-quality impressions, as copies of prints are known. This can be as few as 10 or 20 for a technique like drypoint.

In today's world, however, printmaking technology allows an almost unlimited number of prints to be made with identical quality. To artificially limit the print number to create a sense of urgency or scarcity in an attempt to keep the price high is phony.

When I first started showing my prints in a commercial gallery over a decade ago, I was advised by the owner to limit my editions. For example, my image Dordogne Bridge 118 was limited to only 50 prints. Since then, I have abandoned limited editions, so you would say my prints are now "open editions."

Wikipedia has an excellent article on this topic called: Editions.

COMMENTS

Hi Henry, I completely agree with your assessment about limited editions and giclées. For the past couple of years I have been advocating unlimiting digital reproductions. I've blogged about it on Absolute Arts and made it the feature story of the newsletter that preceded my blog. Likewise, I had a recent blog post titled, "Is Giclée Passé?"

If enough artists and others in the business realize it makes no sense to limit reproductions, it will be a good thing for the art market. Besides, no other form of the arts artificially limits sales of reproductions. It's absurd to imagine allowing only 100,000 people to see a film, or closing a Broadway play while demand was still strong, or a musical act only allowing 10,000 copies of its CDs to be sold.

Keep championing the cause. Best to you! Barney Davey
Posted by: Barney Davey | July 11, 2007 at 12:30 AM

Exclusives, limited editions, etc. seem outdated. It's interesting how the whole design industry has become transparent. With the Internet and the advent of design "do-it-your-self programs" on cable and more—information that previously was "to the trade only" is available to anyone. Technologies have changed and this affects design practices in ways that we could not have predicted earlier.
Posted by: Beth Worthington | July 11, 2007 at 02:04 PM

TOO MANY ARTISTS SPOIL THE POT

We have all heard the proverb, "Too many cooks spoil the pot."

Just as too many cooks can spoil the pot, I believe too many artists can spoil the design.

Having the work of a single artist in a hospital or clinic can provide a unifying design element. With a single artist there is often an apparent style and color palette that ties the different pieces of art together.

Hospitals frequently present a visually confusing appearance. There are often numerous additions and wings tacked on over the decades.

A chaotic appearance does not enhance the healing environment. Why, then, is it so common to pick the work of several artists rather than one or two?

Local politics must be part of the reason; not wanting to offend anyone.

The most successful installations tend to be created by individuals with a strong clear vision. They demand a cohesive look where the various ingredients of the interior work together.

WHY AVOID CREEPY SUBJECTS?

On Sunday I did a post where I said that butterflies are okay in hospitals, but that most other bugs don't work. According to Ulrich and Gilpin, authors of "Putting Patients First," the same prohibition can be applied to snakes, spiders, and big mammals looking right at you. Basically, they are saying, "Avoid all creepy subjects."

There are two theories to explain this:

• Evolutionary theory
• Emotional congruence theory

Evolutionary theory says that humans have an innate predisposition to respond with stress and fear to creepy things. The idea is that natural selection rewarded our ancestors who avoided getting too close to such things as venomous snakes or spiders.

Emotional congruence theory says that a person's feelings or emotions bias their perceptions of environmental surroundings in ways that match their feelings. The negative emotions experienced by many patients (fear, anger, sadness) causes them to perceive certain subject matter in emotionally equivalent negative stressful ways.

I took a picture of a garden spider that I think is quite beautiful and jewel-like. However, most people have an instinctive revulsion of spiders. The emotional congruence theory would suggest that that revulsion would likely increase if you were a patient.

IS NEW ART BETTER?

Everything has to be new and improved, including our art. In our commercial Western culture, that is the norm.

For the last century, artists have been rewarded the most for creating new art. There is an endless and often bewildering mix of new art produced every year. Just look at what is on display at the Whitney Biennale or Documenta XII. These are two international showcases for the best of contemporary art.

Does this mean that art for hospitals should strive to be new?

If you believe what evidence-based art research is telling us, "new" has nothing to do with the art we should be selecting for hospitals. In fact, landscapes painted 200 years ago would be just fine. Those older landscape paintings would be much better than virtually any of the art on display at the Whitney Biennale.

So where does that leave an artist who wants to create art to go in healing environments? To be satisfied as an artist, we can't simply recreate what has been done before, that would be mere craft—just copying. But on the other hand, it helps to be aware of what art patients respond best to.

ALWAYS AVOID YELLOW?

Is yellow a color that should be avoided in healthcare? Why do you think that? I asked five different experts.

- *Jain Malkin, interior designer and author, of Jain Malkin Inc.*
  It's not a yes or no question. Never use it around an inpatient bed on the headwall, as the reflection can make the skin look jaundiced.

  It is viewed by many as a sunny uplifting color that is cheerful. It is best used (this is my opinion) in a triadic color palette with two other colors of equal value.

  There is physiological data for the primary colors but, except for that, color is highly subjective, related to religion (for some

persons), culture, and other influences. In psychiatric populations, 'experts' on color have contrary things to say, such as it's the
best color for schizophrenics and another saying it's the worst.

- *Dr. Upali Nanda, American Art Resources*
Unfortunately, Henry, I know of no evidence to give you an
answer either way. I know that the CHER produced a CD on
color in architecture, but other than that, I don't think much
research has been done on color in healthcare.

- *Dr. Ruth Brent Tofle, University of Missouri, Department of Architectural Studies*
The answer to your question cannot be given universally. However, I'm attaching a copy of our manuscript.

- *Beth Worthington, Worthington Design, (also my sister)*
In general, pure yellow should not be used. I'm talking about
primary, saturated yellow. For one thing, when light reflects off
yellow, it can make skin colors look jaundiced. It tends to make
people look sick. But softer, buttery, pastel yellows can be great.

    Plus I had that yellow bedroom in sixth grade, and I got too
much yellow in my life, ever since then . . . There are exceptions,
when mixed with other primary colors, yellow works well for a
pediatric population.

- *A healthcare art consultant who preferred to remain anonymous:*
The word 'always' is one I do not use. We do avoid lots of
yellow in healthcare as it is a color that can be interpreted negatively (yellow skin tone = jaundice). Especially avoid in oncology
centers and NICUs. Yellow is also a color that often does not
complement the interior colors chosen for facilities. However, we
do not avoid yellow butterflies, close-up yellow flowers. . . . we are
more likely to avoid yellow fields of flowers, as they set an overall
yellow tone.

Design guidelines that are frequently referred to. These quotes are taken from "Color in Healthcare Environments," by Ruth Brent Tofle, Ph.D.; Benyamin Schwarz, Ph.D.; So-Yeon,Yoon, MA; Andrea Max-Royale, M.E.Des.

Leibrock (2000)

Yellow to green tones should be avoided because they are associated with body fluids. Yellow, green, and purple colors are not flattering to the skin and reflect jaundiced skin tones (Gappell, 1990). . . . Yellow color schemes may cause difficulties for people who have yellowing lenses. Bright yellow colors can intensify to the point of annoying. Primary colors (red, yellow, and blue) and strong patterns are pleasing at first but may eventually become tiring.

Spivack (1984)

Institutional bathrooms often create a context filled with fecal and urine associations, for instance by using dark or brown tiled surfaces and/or dirty yellow paint under dim lighting . . . Colors should support accurate skin-tone perception . . . Yellows, greens and blues are particularly to be avoided as non-accent wall (background) hues.

Marberry & agon (1995), Marberry (1997)

Its nature symbol is the sun, defined often by its qualities of optimism, clarity, and intellect. Bright yellow is often noted for its mood-enhancing properties. Yellow must be carefully applied in certain settings, as it causes thought associations of aging and yellow skin tones associated with jaundice.

Malkin (1982, 1992)

Red and yellows, for example, should be used in settings where creative activity is desired and socialization encouraged.

Brawley (1997)

Yellow evokes a sense of energy and excitement and its brilliance is most often associated with the sun. The emotional effects of yellow are optimistic and bright, yet sometimes unsettling and seldom restful. Yellow reflects more light than any other color and can be used to increase illumination in poorly lighted areas.

I'M AN ARTIST, NOT A PHOTOGRAPHER

"You're very different than the other photographers I work with," an art consultant from Philadelphia said to me yesterday. I explained that one difference is that I don't consider myself a photographer. I see myself as an artist, who happens to use a camera.

What's the difference between professional artists and photographers?

- Artists go to art school.
  Photographers attend journalism or photography school.
- Artists have studied art history, drawing, and painting.
  Photographers have studied journalism, writing, and studio techniques.
- Artists learn how to create an engaging image on a blank canvas.
  Photographers learn how to tell stories with their pictures.
- Artists follow their intuition to create bodies of work.
  Photographers take assignments to go out on shoots.
- Artists want the final image to be visually successful whatever it takes.
  Photographers want their work to be an accurate document.
- Artists create big images that can hang on walls.
  Photographers create small images that work for layouts in print.
- Artists tend to be obsessed with content.
  Photographers tend to be obsessed with craft.

I DON'T DO SUNSETS

It is easy to drift into creating clichés when making nature art for healthcare. Sunsets must be the ultimate cliché; I don't do sunsets.

Just before leaving for our trip to Sanibel, I had lunch with Deanna

Dikeman, a good friend and one of the best art photographers in the Midwest. We talked about how nature photography tends to be decorative, rather than serious. "Decorative" is not a word most artists would want associated with their work. Even the words "beautiful" and "pretty" would make most artists cringe.

The words "decorative" and "beauty" imply shallowness. It seems that great works of art need to be innovative. Serious fine art must have a great concept behind it. How can one be innovative when taking photographs of sunsets? It is hard enough being innovative with nature images. Perhaps the most one can hope for is to be fresh.

COMMENTS

Hey, I must disagree. Beauty doesn't imply shallowness—but decorative might.

Posted by: Deanna Dikeman | December 11, 2007 at 04:05 PM

Henry, should I be asking myself if my nature photos are decorative or beautiful or innovative or serious or fresh? Actually, the bottom line for what I do is the answer to this question: Do my photos have a positive effect on the patients? If the answer is yes, then I have succeeded in creating appropriate healing art. That's enough for me . . . A note about sunsets—I don't do many sunsets either, but for a different reason. As a sunset portrays the end of a day, some patients associate a sunset with the end of a life. We have to be careful with placing sunsets in healthcare facilities . . .

Posted by: Elaine Poggi | December 11, 2007 at 07:36 PM

RESOLUTION IS OVERRATED

For photographic prints, it would seem that higher resolution is better, right? Most people would pick a high-resolution image.

Current fine art inkjet printers have gotten so good that I no longer think that greater resolution makes a difference.

The printer I just added to my studio a few weeks ago (the Epson Stylus Pro 11880) has the ability to print as fine as 2,880 dots-per-inch. I ran some tests where I printed the same detailed landscape image on matte paper at different resolutions. I then had a couple of people look carefully at the images to pick the best. The viewers did not know which prints were at which resolution.

The result: It was almost impossible to tell the prints apart whether they were 360 dots-per-inch or 2,880 dots-per-inch. They all looked perfect.

When looking very closely, one viewer did correctly pick the 360 dots-per-inch print as being slightly softer in appearance.

Conclusion: Printing at 720 dots-per-inch is ideal for inkjet prints.

I suspect that if the test was done on glossy paper, the higher resolution might be visible on close inspection. But in the real world, no one will ever be able to see any difference.

For years I have observed that photographers look at prints differently than other people. Photographers tend to look at different distances. Most photographers end up putting their face within a couple of inches to inspect the print. I don't think non-photographers ever do this.

One advantage of printing at lower resolution is that the prints come out much faster.

TAKE IT, IT'S GOOD FOR YOU!

Kids used to be forced to take cod liver oil because experts said it was good for you. It has been described as having the intense and obnoxious odor of rotten fish and rancid oil.

Sometimes I think connoisseurs are doing the same thing when they make the general public look at art they don't like. They feel it is their responsibility to educate those whose tastes are not as advanced. In schools, galleries, and museums, I can accept that argument, but not in hospitals.

It is wrong to make people in hospitals look at art they don't like. There are enough other unpleasant things going on that increase discomfort. We don't need to add art to the list.

It is very clear what people don't like. This has been studied hundreds of times in countries all over the world. Regular people don't like abstract art.

This post was prompted by listening to a new CD that I just bought: Gloria Cheng's Piano Music of Salonen, Stucky & Lutoslawski. After I was half-way through the disc, I realized I was listening to it because it was good for me, not because I enjoyed it. Perhaps in time I will learn to appreciate it, but meanwhile I switched to Scarlatti: Keyboard Sonatas played by Andras Schiff. Within seconds of putting it on, I started to feel more relaxed. The dogs even came back into the room.

COMMENTS

As someone who creates a lot of abstract art, I obviously don't buy the idea that all abstract art is like cod liver oil, something that is forced on many people. It's just not as simple as abstract is bad, and realistic is good. I've seen abstract art that I hate, and abstract art that moves me. I've seen realistic art that is beautiful, and realistic art that is trite and overly nostalgic. The quality and appropriateness of an art piece goes well beyond the simple category it sits in.
Posted by: Daniel Sroka | August 04, 2008 at 11:35 AM

Daniel, I agree with you. I've oversimplified to make my point. To lump all abstract art into one big lump just does not fit with the real world. However, if you look at the many studies that have been done on preferences, abstract art is at the bottom.

Also, regarding your art, I know you are calling it "abstract," but in fact you are showing objective photographs of nature. You explore shallow depth of focus and very tight framing to pull out the patterns, textures, and colors found in nature.

In a sense, you are "abstracting" nature, pulling out the most important features of your subject, but that does not make them purely abstract. At least not the way I understand the word.
Posted by: Henry Domke | August 04, 2008 at 02:39 PM

IS ABSTRACT ART RELEVANT TODAY?

The use of abstract art in healthcare is controversial. But where does abstract art fit in the larger art world, beyond the walls of hospitals? The exhibit "Action/Abstraction: Pollock, de Kooning, and American Art, 1940–1976" at the St. Louis Art Museum has me ruminating on the history of abstract art and its place today.

My conclusion: Abstract art is now a minor player in the confusing jumble of contemporary art.

Richard Kalina wrote in the September issue of Art in America:

Does...abstraction have anything to tell us about today? In what ways . . . does this relate to the problems we face in a much larger and more complex art world? Art now seems to have no boundaries, literally and figuratively. Art is made and displayed virtually anywhere in an exponentially expanding art world of art fairs, biennials...the Internet...essentially in any form conceivable.

On the one hand this is liberating, on the other it is confusing.

It is confusing! It would be so much easier if there was truth in art like the time period covered by this exhibit (1940–1976). During that era, art critics Clement Greenberg and Harold Rosenburg wrote convincing essays about right and wrong. They believed there was one right truth about art. Many artists and art connoisseurs believed them.

Today, that is all gone, and abstract art is now merely one of a thousand possible answers for what art can be. I miss that era of certainty!

COMMENTS

Two thoughts.

Does "abstract art" really mean anything other than art since the beginning of the 20th century? Since then, even if one practices "representational art," one really can't be unaware of the ironies in doing so, because the world has been changed by the advent of abstraction and we really can't undo it. Everything now takes place in a context of abstraction.

Second, I tend to think of the word "abstract" as having some meaning in the philosophical sense, as in "ideal" and not "real." I think this may be a bad habit, because it really doesn't work very well. Philosophically the opposite of abstract is concrete. In art, "abstract" happens to be very much about the concrete presence of materials, so much so that the term "abstract" can't have much meaning in the philosophic sense.

What are you left with then? At this point I'm trying on the notion that it's really a term of chronology, more than anything designating an era. This is a provocative stance because it challenges my idea of representational art. The idea that representational art is simply anything that has a recognizable object in it really isn't of much use anyway. Can any artist working today who isn't entirely naive avoid considering her work through a lens of abstraction? I don't think so.

Henry, you, for instance, talk about getting your work to "sing." I think that way of looking at things is drenched in early 20th century ideas of abstraction of representing sound through color. You are working on matters that are very likely not much to do with recognition, but rather with feel.

I've said too much, but one more thing. I think the ab-ex-ists are ab-fab and I will be fascinated by them forever. I went to an ab-ex school. I was taught by them, and I am one at heart. De Kooning, you might know, will claim a sort of representational bent to his work, which he spoke of as a journal to his days movements.

When asked to explain his abstract expressionist images (de Kooning) said that he was most fascinated by the quick glimpses of things as he moved about the city, and when back in the studio he found he would slip back into those fleeting images. He said, "If you want to describe my work, call me a slipping glimpser." (Alan Peterson)

De Kooning clearly was not interested in a Platonic ideal, and he may have had a keener interest in representation than most contemporary nature photographers, who are generally interested in "abstract" qualities of light, tone, and rhythm.
Posted by: Bill Knight | October 03, 2008 at 08:07 AM

Health or illness is reminiscent of the zeros and ones of computer science. You either have it or you don't. The very fact that people argue about abstract art probably indicates there can be no object contribution of abstract art to health. It is easier to see the contribution of, say, animals to health. Some people are frightened of velvet clown paintings. Some are disgusted, and heaven help us, some people buy velvet clown paintings as "art."
Posted by: kudzu fire | November 16, 2008 at 06:01 PM

INTERVIEWS

ART FOR BRIGHAM AND WOMEN'S HOSPITAL

Brigham and Women's Hospital, which is affiliated with Harvard Medical School, is one of the best hospitals in the world. U.S. News and World Report calls Brigham and Women's Hospital the 10th best hospital in the United States.

I thought it would be interesting to find out how they went about selecting art for one of their new projects, the Carl J. and Ruth Shapiro Cardiovascular Center. I called Michelle Jannine Rheaume, their art coordinator, and asked her a few questions.

Tell me a little about yourself; what is your background?

I'm a recent graduate of the Massachusetts College of Art and Design. My focus was on painting and art history. I was hired a year ago as an intern to help develop their archive database. Now I'm full-time.

Did you consider research on evidence-based art when you selected this work?

No. But we are looking at that for future projects. It seems that finding good evidence is like finding a needle in a haystack.

One of the objectives with this collection was to have it fit with the sleek contemporary architecture.

Who made the decision on what art to select? Was it an art committee?

It was a small group: four Brigham and Women's Hospital senior staff, one of the donors, and the art consultant, Elizabeth Erdreich.

The hospital also has a formal art committee that meets quarterly. They also helped.

Who paid for this art? What did it cost?

We spent $600,000 for the art. $500,000 was in the construction budget, and then a donor came forward with another $100,000 to complete the project.

What has the response been from the patients?

We've only been open two weeks, so it is too early to say. However, we are going to be doing surveys to assess patient response to the art.

I see that you worked closely with Erdreich White Fine Art on this project. How did you happen to pick them?

The job was put out to bid among regional art consultants. A few were interviewed and Elizabeth Erdreich was selected. This was before I started working here.

HEALTH ENVIRONMENT ART SERVICES

I first met Denise Rippinger at the Healthcare Design Conference in 2005 in Scottsdale. I was pretty inexperienced at providing art for hospitals at that point. She was kind enough to introduce me to people and explain what she did as an art consultant. Recently, she moved to a new office, so I thought it would be a good time to find out what's new.

Tell me about Health Environment Art Services. How long have you been in business?

This year is our 20th anniversary. I started the first company, Corporate Artworks Ltd., in 1988. Coming from a business background, having a love and passion for art, as well as being an artist, is what gave me the idea to start this business. If you recall, in the early 80s, art did not yet play a big part in the office environment or hospitals.

In the beginning, all of my clients were corporate offices, and then gradually I started getting requests to improve healthcare environments. It seemed like a natural thing to do, and I found that it gave me great pleasure to have an audience that not only enjoyed the art, but that gave art a deeper meaning and purpose.

How many people work there?

Currently we have 21 people on staff, and this is our third facility due to growth. In 2003, we officially started a new company called 'Health Environment Art Services.' Although we had been placing artwork in hospitals and healthcare environments for many years, the stigma of 'corporate' did not give us the credibility that we deserved.

I understand you have recently moved. Tell me about your new place.

Our facility has a beautiful showroom and great areas set up specifically for our art consultants to design projects. We also have office space, frame styling, frame shop, shipping and receiving. It is quite a busy operation with anywhere from 30 to 50 jobs going on at the same time. Our new facility houses both companies.

Since you are based in Chicago, do you work primarily in the upper Midwest?

We work with clients nationwide.

Can you tell me a bit about your Creative Solutions Team?

We pride ourselves on creating higher levels of healing environments that are unique. We have formed a 'Creative Solutions Team,' in essence a brainstorming team made up of very experienced art consultants, interior designers, art degree graduates, and artists. It allows everyone to express their creative ideas for a specific project, and as a team we expand on those ideas. It's a great thing for our clients because they know that their space is going to be special.

What are your thoughts on evidence-based art?

I am often asked what my thoughts are about evidence-based art. This is a tough question because I feel like this has become an industry buzz phrase.

In reality, what might be comforting or distracting to one person could be the total opposite to another. Ethnicity, age, demographics, and religion are just a few elements that can throw a wrench into the evidence-based philosophy. What works for some doesn't work for everyone.

I think that every hospital needs to be looked at individually, and the artwork based specifically on its patient population. This is not to throw research out the window, but to use common sense. Whether it is evidence-based or not, I personally think that nature is the source for all healing.

INTERVIEW WITH JOAN SWENSON

Last week I had a phone conversation with Joan Swenson of Artscape, a healthcare art consulting company.

Tell me a little about Artscape.

We started as a healthcare art consulting firm in Philadelphia in 1981. Most of our jobs have been in the Northeast, but we are looking at expanding. We have 10 people on staff and work out of an 8,000-sq-ft warehouse. In addition to art consulting, we also have a full-service frame shop.

What percentage of your work is healthcare?

80 percent. We also do some corporate work.

What are your thoughts on evidence-based art?

A hospital is an organic entity with a personality. Our job is to draw that out of our clients and make that personality come alive through art. In one way, that expression of personality can be used for branding. In a more meaningful way, the art should reflect hospitals as sacred places. I say 'sacred places,' because hospitals are where people are born and die. We are at our most vulnerable when we are in hospitals, so the art needs to respect the depth of that experience for both staff and patient families.

My biggest concern is that evidence-based art oversimplifies the complexity of the selection of artwork programs. Artwork must be selected that considers the complexity of hospital spaces, as well as their persona.

Let me make an analogy. Is it good to eat only vegetables or only protein? Of course not. In the same sense, is it good to show people only images of nature?"

I remember once that you told me you enjoyed chemistry in high school, but decided to go into interior design. What was your path to becoming an art consultant?

When I graduated from high school in 1971, I was doing very well academically, I loved chemistry, loved singing and science, and I was in the National Honor Society. But rather than encourage me to pursue a career in science or medicine, the guidance counselor encouraged me to go into design.

Why?

She said, 'You should be a designer since you wear such cool clothing.' So I started at Boston University and studied fine and applied arts. My focus was on music and psychology. Combining them in a career (such as music therapy) was not an option then. My mother discouraged me from going into music, telling me that 'It was a hard row to hoe,' so I followed my next love, which was design.

At that time, about 60 percent of the architects in Boston were unemployed, so instead of pursuing architecture, I got an M.F.A. in interior design. As a college student, I got a job with Art for Industry, an art leasing company. It was wonderful work. I found that I really liked the art part of the work. Then I got an internship working in the galleries at Lincoln Center. I was sold. I loved working with art. I loved the art and I loved the people.

In 1976, I was floating in a pool at my brother's home in North Carolina and an idea came to me. I realized I wanted to create a national art leasing company, and I wanted to call it Artscape. In 1978, we moved to Philadelphia, and I got a job managing an art gallery that had a frame shop. That is where I learned about framing.

In 1981, I started Artscape. Right from the beginning we did healthcare. My second job was to provide art for an 11-story hospital. This was before art was common in hospitals. Through word-of-mouth, the business took off.

I have had other side businesses over the years, but the core work that I have done for the last 27 years is to be an art consultant for healthcare.

For more information, visit www.artscapeusa.com.

INTERVIEW WITH ANNETTE RIDENOUR

Annette Ridenour is one of the top leaders in the use of art in healthcare. She is also one of the founders and leaders of the Society for Arts in Healthcare. She was on the board of SAH since the beginning and served as its president for two terms. I wanted to get her impression of their annual conference this year.

What was your overall impression of the SAH conference in Philadelphia this year?

I believe that SAH should be spending more time on the visual arts and less time on performance arts. With the huge construction boom in healthcare, there is a tremendous need for high quality visual arts programs.

Was there anything that caught your eye at the conference?

There was a fascinating art-making program for children from Robert Rothschild and Jay at the University of Florida at Gainesville. It makes it easy for hospitalized kids over the age of 3 to create images on screen. These images can then be displayed on their screen, shared with others, or put in virtual galleries on-line.

SEEWALL Studios had a great booth and a fascinating product that we are going to start to use. SEEWALL merges art and technology in a multimedia display of color, sound, and light and motion. Brilliant seascapes invite children and families into a multimedia exploration.

Last, but not least, is the Blair Sadler Awards. The five winners this year had some incredible projects. For example, one showed how music therapy in a burn unit could reduce pain substantially.

Another showed how dance could get pregnant women in the ghetto to be more involved with prenatal care and have improved outcomes. More information about this year's and former winners and how to apply for 2009 can be found on the SAH website.

Tell me a little about your upcoming book about art in healthcare. Who is your intended audience?

We intend this to be used by hospital leadership, artists, and the public. For hospital leadership we (she is writing with Blair Sadler) will explain the business case for art—for artists we want to show them the possibilities to help them see what is needed. Lastly, we want to explain to the public how important the arts can be in healthcare.

PLANETREE NETWORK—THE BIRTH OF PATIENT-CENTERED CARE

As soon as I started learning about the use of art in healthcare, I kept hearing the name, "Planetree Network." The book that has been repeatedly recommended to me by experts in the field ("Putting Patients First") is a publication of the Planetree Alliance. To find out more, I asked Kimberly Nelson Montague, director of design consultation at Planetree, a few questions.

What is the primary purpose of Planetree Network?

In short, we are a non-profit membership organization that works with hospitals and healthcare centers to develop and implement patient-centered care in healing environments.

How does it relate to the other non-profit organizations involved with healthcare design? Complementary? Competition? Different angle?

Since we are a membership-based organization for hospitals and healthcare systems, we serve as a catalyst and partner in developing environments that are not only patient-centered, but holistic, value-based and support the safety of patients as well. Planetree was founded by a patient; truly unique, I believe, amongst other healthcare design organizations.

How many people are in the Planetree Network?

We have over 125 affiliate member sites, from the East Coast to the West, including Canada and the Netherlands.

How can you help interior designers who pick art for healthcare?

We often work with our affiliates' architects and interior designers on new and ongoing projects at their sites, although our focus is on assisting the affiliate member, not the interior designer, on implementing the Planetree Model of Care. Certainly, by becoming more familiar with the 10 core components, the interior designers will learn more about how the environment can either inhibit or enhance the experience for patients, families, and staff.

How can you help facilities people involved with making decisions about art for healthcare?

There are many references in the market regarding choices for artwork in healthcare facilities. The book, 'Putting Patients First,' talks about artwork choices in a healthcare environment. The Center for Health Design also has resources available to facilities managers and directors. Artwork, albeit a personal choice, can play a major role in the first impressions at a hospital, as well as provide for therapeutic distractions for patients while interned there.

Do you have any conferences or events where art is one of the key topics?

No specific conferences that I can think of. However, artwork is always a major topic at the Annual Planetree Conference!

TEN QUESTIONS FOR BETH WORTHINGTON

Today I am trying something new; I'm going to include a phone interview recorded using Skype. I called an experienced designer from St. Louis, Beth Worthington (who is also my sister). She has decades of experience in design, and a lot of that has been in healthcare.

When you are asked to select art for a client, how do you go about it?

I am usually involved with the design already, so I know what is needed. I know the colors and finishes, I know the client, and I know who will be using the space.

How has the Internet changed the way you select art?

For the last few years, I have increasingly gone to the web to do research to help find the art. Ninety percent of my search for art is on the web. Even if I want to use a local gallery, I will go to their website. When I want to use international art, I have been using Novica.

How often do you specify art without actually seeing the real thing?

Maybe 65–70 percent of the time. But some of that may be seeing samples.

There is a trend to use more nature photography in healthcare. Do you think this is a passing fad?

It is hard to make assumptions about the future, but I do not think nature photography in healthcare is a passing fad.

Who are your interior design heroes?

I like contemporary spaces and fresh approaches. Here are three of my favorites.
- Andre Putnam
- John Saladino
- David Rockwell

What advice do you have for artists who want to sell their products to hospitals?

You need to be a good business person; you have to follow up. You have to understand what your client wants. You have to understand how to market your work and think in creative ways about how to reach your clients; it is critical to use the current tools (web, computer, email).

What are the most common mistakes that hospitals and clinics make when buying art?

Because art is the last thing to be installed, hospitals allow the art budget to be cut to take care of cost overruns elsewhere. Therefore, art suffers.

Another problem is that the art can be 'dumbed down.' People try to make it so universally palatable that it becomes wall furniture; it's there to fill a space.

How has the use of photography changed over your career?

Photography has increasingly become more popular. And now, with digital imaging, the prints are bigger and other material is being used to print on.

How different are the healthcare art needs in St. Louis from those in Palo Alto, Los Angeles, London, Munich, or Seoul?

Art can help give people a sense of place, so considering regional art may be appropriate, but for many projects there are other needs.

Would you ever buy your art from someone overseas?

Yes. See question 2.

ART FOR MILITARY HOSPITALS (PART 1)

What is unique about art intended for military hospitals? To help answer that question, I asked Kathy Hathorn, president and principal-in-charge of American Art Resources, to share some of her insight.

Is the selection of art for military hospitals different from civilian hospitals?

Most of our military work has been for the Air Force. Yes, I do believe that there are some important issues to consider.

Since the U.S. has an all-volunteer army, its facilities need to have appealing, psychologically supportive spaces. They are moving toward a first-class look. I see this with not only the military health-care facility itself, but also residential spaces, especially for foreign service personnel.

What about the fact that many of those in military hospitals these days tend to be young soldiers injured in the line of duty?

Clearly this is a different population than you would see at a general medical hospital. It is better to think of their needs as one would think about a specialty hospital like a Shriners Hospital or a hospital specializing in stroke care. For one thing, their length of stay tends to be longer. In a general medical hospital people might average three or four days. Soldiers recovering from battlefield injuries might be hospitalized for months. That makes the art on the wall even more important; they will be living with it for longer.

Are there other issues to consider?
One can't ignore those who are not combatants, as well as the families of those who are at war. They, too, suffer and need medical help. There is a growing incidence of post-traumatic stress disorder. To help deal with this we need better research.

Speaking of research, the appropriate use of art in military hospitals seems like it would be prime for some evidence-based design research.
I agree. Not much research has been done on this topic so far.

SAN DIEGO HEALTHCARE ART PROGRAM

April Game wants to connect regional artists to people that live in San Diego. To do this, she started the nonprofit San Diego Fine Art Society nine months ago. I talked with her about it on the phone today.

Tell me a little bit about the idea behind the San Diego Fine Art Society.
When I left the commercial art world of Los Angeles and moved to San Diego two years ago, I asked, 'What does San Diego need?' Since I know many artists (I have more than 1,000 in my database), I realized that there is a critical need for artists to be mentored in their business life. At the same time, there are a lot of educated, affluent people in the San Diego area who are interested in art, but don't buy locally. My goal is to connect these regional artists to the public.

How do you do that?
One way is we hold events. I coach the artists on how to present their work. They are given five minutes to present themselves to the public, to explain what they are about. Also at these events, we have

lectures to help buyers understand what is involved with starting to create a collection of original art.

I see on your website that one of the areas you focus on is art for healthcare. Tell me about that.

We are starting to act as an art consulting service for hospitals and clinics, especially for the needy. Our first big project is with Fran Butler-Cohen. She is the CEO of eight free medical clinics in the San Diego area. Her goal is to help those who feel pain to not feel pain. She has selected us to help create a healing environment that will help reduce the suffering. This will involve art, sculpture, colors on the wall, and even music.

How is that going to be funded?

We are going to have a gala event this fall for 350 people. We have already lined up some local sponsors. Our goal is to raise $100,000 for this project. We are also exploring getting grants. Our hope is to be a model for providing art to free clinics across the country.

How big is the organization?

At this time, we have six volunteers and no paid staff, but we are growing rapidly.

LEIGH FOGLE INTERVIEW

Leigh Fogle owns and manages one of the fastest growing companies involved with art for healthcare in the Southeast, Fogle Fine Art. I called her this week to ask her some questions about the business.

How has the current economic downturn affected your business?

We started seeing a slowdown in the third quarter of 2007. Small companies like ours started to feel the downturn before the larger companies got hit.

Our business has three sides: retail, corporate, and healthcare. The corporate work has had the biggest hit, especially the banks. Our bank business is gone. High-end retail has remained strong.

Our healthcare business is fine. However, we are bracing for a possible downturn in healthcare art budgets over the next few years. Hospital construction will continue, but if inflation goes up (as we expect), then the hospitals will have less money to devote to art. Art budgets will be cut.

Tell me a little about Fogle Fine Art. How did you get into this?
I started college at DePauw University with a major in economics; I've always loved numbers. But numbers weren't enough. I love working with people and I love art, so I switched to Indiana University. There I earned a B.A. with a degree as an art history major. I minored in psychology and studio art.

Right after graduation, my husband, a musician, convinced me to move to Jacksonville.

How did the company start and how has it changed over the years?
In 1994, one year after moving to Jacksonville, I started Leigh Fogle Fine Art. I bought a used mat-cutter and my husband, Bryan, and I started the business in our house. Our focus was providing framing and poster art for corporate clients.

In 1996, we got an SBA loan and leased 3,600 square feet of office space. We also changed the name to Fogle Fine Art and Accessories. Business grew rapidly, so in 2001 we leased the adjacent office to expand our space to 6,000 square feet.

Healthcare became an increasing focus starting in 2003. Jacksonville was a referral hub for healthcare with facilities like Mayo Clinic and Shands. We worked with them, and that became a special interest of mine.

In 2005, we moved to our current location. It is bigger (10,000 square feet), and it is in a better location to hold events (we have a lot of events in the gallery).

Why are you drawn to art for healthcare?
My interest goes back many years. Even in the 7th grade, I remember writing a school paper on the psychological impact

of color. With my background in art and psychology in college, I considered art therapy as a career move in 1994.

Art in hospitals affects people more than corporate art. I don't treat it as a 'product,' but rather I approach the work as a partner with the hospital. Often I involve local artists to reach out to the community.

How has your staffing changed over the years?

In 1994, there were just two of us. In 1996, we expanded to four. In 2001, we had grown to 12 employees, but most of them were part-time. Today, we have eight full-time employees and two or more part-time employees. We intentionally want to stay small. I want to stay small enough to be 'hands on.'

What geographic area do you serve?

We serve the entire Southeastern United States and plan to stay within that region. Since framing is such a big part of our business (60–70 percent), shipping the framed art becomes a major issue. By focusing on the Southeast, we can keep down shipping costs and be more available to our clients.

Recently my husband got a full-time job as a songwriter in Nashville. This means I will be spending more time in Nashville, which is perfect to better serve the Southeast. I had already been working with companies based in Nashville. Now, I can better serve them.

What percentage of your business is healthcare?

20 to 25 percent and growing.

Do you refer to evidence-based art when helping a healthcare client come up with an art program?

I am not an expert on evidence-based design yet, but I'm learning about it. I tend to go with my gut and my background in art history.

I am aware of the studies done at Texas A&M showing that art depicting clear, unambiguous nature scenes helps patients recover faster and with less pain medication. Crisp, clear photographs are always powerful, as the viewer can put themselves into the picture, so to speak.

Some research on evidence-based art suggests that abstract art is inappropriate for patient care areas. What is your opinion?

Even though I like abstract art, I agree. In patient care areas representational art that is calm and peaceful is important. But I think that even more important than subject matter is color. Blues and greens are the colors of nature and work much better in healthcare.

In other parts of the hospital, I think it is fine to bring in abstraction. Often I like to see a transition to abstraction when going from patient care areas to public areas. One way to do this is to use representational images of nature close up and hence, tend to read as abstract, like images of water.

For more information, go to www.foglefineart.com.

ICU ART SO BAD I WANTED TO COVER IT WITH A TOWEL

My good friend and fellow photographer Vaughn Wascovich was hospitalized this week. I wanted to get his perspective on what the art experience was like as he lay there in his intensive care unit bed for two days. He was in a brand new ICU room in a hospital close to Dallas.

What art did you see, what was it like?

I was really disturbed by the art. There was only one black-and-white print, a studio shot of a flower. Where I lay in bed, I had no choice but to look at it. It was so bad I wanted to cover it with a towel.

Why did it bother you so much?

The flower was obviously a studio shot with a white background. It seemed anemic, like me. It seemed disconnected, and since I felt disconnected, that was bad. I care about home and place, and this picture did not put me there; it bothered me.

You mentioned that it was black and white. Do you think that made it worse for you?

I can't say; normally, I love black-and-white photography. But in this setting it seemed dated, disconnected, and not organic. Nothing around me was organic, even my limited view out the window was a parking lot.

When I was in bed I had very few options about what to look at; it's the clock, the TV, or the art. The TV just made me feel worse. All the ads seemed to be about food. Since I couldn't eat, that was very stressful. A Wendy's hamburger never looked so good...

I should have brought my iPod; that would have helped a lot. I could have closed my eyes and listened to music.

What art would you have liked?

I'm drawn to landscapes, but not one by that Painter-of-Light guy, what's his name...(Thomas Kinkade). His pictures show beauty as a fantasy; they are not real. I wanted to be connected to the real world.

What was it like when you got out?

I went to a local garden and that helped tremendously. I touched and smelled the plants. It really felt good.

COMMENTS

It's not just the art that's present...it's the lack of virtually anything that is not starkly clinical. The room is so incredibly institutional; it has always amazed me that birthing rooms have been made to seem more family-like or family-oriented, but rooms for adults that are ill enough to be hospitalized remain boring and mundane. White walls, large-numeraled black-rimmed analog clocks, single-tiered laminated shelves, and often the lone, sun-bleached, uninspired print. Environmentally uninspiring for anyone that is there for treatment, and it has to be depressing for those who work there daily.

Posted by: John Storjohann | September 18, 2008 at 06:39 AM

I spent a week in the hospital recently, and every day I thought of you and your blog, Henry, because of the photograph in my room there. It was a bleak landscape with fog or mist in the background that obscured everything. The colors were dark blues and browns, and I found it depressing. I wish I could have had one of your bright and cheery images to look at instead!

The view out the window was of another building, but I could see a small patch of sky, and that was my saving grace.

When I was discharged and went outside for the first time in a week, everything seemed too bright and too colorful. It was overwhelming, and I almost had to close my eyes. I guess it was from a week of sensory deprivation. I had never experienced that before, and was surprised by it.

Posted by: Cassie | September 28, 2008 at 09:52 PM

Thanks for letting us know about your experience. Your real world experience (and Vaughn's) supports my belief that patients have special needs for what they are given to see. The value of the proper art, a view to nature and daylight are all meaningful.

Posted by: Henry Domke | October 01, 2008 at 09:14 AM

I had a breast cancer scare a few weeks ago and spent several tense hours at the Barnes Center for Advanced Medicine. I've always had a great experience with their breast health set up there—runs very smoothly and the people are friendly, etc.—but in the hall and rooms you go to for further testing, the art was atrocious! And I really noticed it because I kept going back in for mammograms, then they'd make me sit in a waiting area with really dreadful pictures on the wall—one was a landscape winter image—especially bleak. The only really great piece was a mosaic done by breast cancer survivors, which was really creative and heart-warming. But even in the exam rooms they had blurry pictures of dandelions. At first I assumed that I was being hyper-sensitive to the art issue, but I have to believe that other women have the same reaction.

It was a very scary, surreal experience, and the art made it worse!! You're in a waiting room or exam room, with your thoughts going wild, with nothing to look at but old magazines—it's a recipe for disaster.

Posted by: Kim Reiss | October 03, 2008 at 10:38 AM

TARA HILL DISCUSSES COLOR IN HEALTHCARE

Tara Hill discussed how to best use color in hospitals in the Sept./
Oct. 2008 issue of Healthcare Construction & Operations magazine.
Hill is a recognized expert in the use of color in healthcare.

When asked about interior colors for adult patients, she wrote:

> I always go back to the patient population and what is appro-
> priate for each population. If the population can withstand
> saturated color, I find that people respond to a stimulating
> environment. The quickest and easiest way to create a stimu-
> lating environment is with colors. We know that a stimulating
> environment often promotes healing.

Tara R. Hill, ASID, is a registered interior designer and founder
of LittleFISH Think Tank.

INTERVIEW: DIANA SPELLMAN

Diana Spellman is one of the leaders of art in healthcare. Last year,
she wrote a cover article, "The Art of Healing," for Healthcare
Design magazine. Recently, she answered a few questions about her
company and the use of art in healthcare during a phone interview.

**Last year you were diagnosed and treated for breast cancer. Has that
experience altered your view on the use of art in healthcare?**
Yes! I've become more passionate about the use of color and artwork
in healthcare facilities; the mind, body, and spirit connection is very
real. For instance, I received chemotherapy for five months with an
excellent team of doctors, but the infusion area where I spent a lot
of time was painted in gray blue tones that did not take advantage
of the wide expanse of windows, and the artwork consisted of several
silk wreaths. Fortunately, I had a very positive and fighting spirit, but
the patient care environment does have a significant influence on the
patient's state of mind, thus affecting their health.

I witnessed many patients come into the chemotherapy area,

completely down in spirit and really scared. I believe that if the environment utilized warmth in neutral wall finishes, allowed the sunlight and nature outdoors to come into the space, and utilized interesting macro images of nature within the spaces, a sense of positive hope would transcend full circle to the patients and caregivers.

In addition, I was hospitalized numerous times for surgeries, again experiencing firsthand how the built environment affects the patient experience, as well as my family and the caregivers. The exterior/interior environments from the time you leave your car, cross the parking and enter the building, the color, materials and artwork affect your sense of security and well being. An example of this was my experience of pre-op prep in an area that had a sense of coldness, from the use of hard materials in grayed/cool colors, cool lighting color that made the patient feel like a specimen, and lastly no artwork of any vibrancy and clarity with color. Henry, that is something your work brings to the environment, a true sense of hope and compassion.

One last example of an experience I encountered was my hospital room, right out of the retro 60s with the built-in lockers for my clothes and an attempt to update with paint and a pastel wallpaper border. The paint selection and the use of a beautiful image of nature, say an up-close branch with a butterfly, brings into the space a special sense of nature's surprises. As a patient, I would have felt more cherished had I not been looking at a wall that was crowded with numerous signs and marker boards, that I could not even see without putting on my glasses.

What impact will the downturn in the economy have on the use of art in healthcare? Does this mean reduced budgets and more poster art?
There is no doubt that people will continue to cut budgets; money is tighter. With less money for art, I encourage my clients to do less, but do it with the most sensitive impact possible. Rather than buy more quantity and inexpensive, plan on blending the budget with fine artwork in the key wayfinding focal points, and if needed, implementing it in phases over time.

I am very proud to say that many times we have helped our owners create events to raise dollars to fund the better quality artwork; we are there to really partner with the owner. An example of this was several years ago, I created a wine and cheese fundraiser for an owner, and we did a private fine art preview tour with community leaders. It was so much fun! We had the help of an auctioneer to auction off 'naming rights' on the specialized pieces, and we helped to raise over 40 percent of their entire artwork budget in a two-hour period.

Many hospital CEOs understand the value of working with design professionals to create the healing environments—with artwork master plans. If they read the latest information on this topic or have completed new buildings or renovations with well-thought artwork, they experience dividends with their patient satisfaction, thus it translates into more market share. That being said, it is more critical than ever to work with experienced professionals that understand the administration's mission and goals. The artwork budgets must be carefully planned and executed to get the most value for the dollar. No owner has money to waste; that is why working with a professional creates the most successful end results.

Tell me a little about Spellman Brady & Company. How did you get into this, how did the company start and how has it changed over the years? Who is the "Brady" part of the name?

Brady is my maiden name. I like it and am proud of it, so I wanted to utilize it in our company's identity. We are also a certified WBE (woman-owned enterprise), so again it was important to use the Brady name. I grew up in a medical family, but always loved design and art. I love to create artwork, but that tapered off as I became busy with my career and family. My husband, Stan, and I got into the healthcare design specialty 28 years ago working with the large architectural firm HLM. That is where we met each other, working in the interiors department, and have moved cross country twice during our careers, working out in the inter-mountain west and also California.

How many people work there now?

The first four years in business, Stan and I worked out of our home with a part-time assistant, but it became too much of an invasion on our family (I was expecting our second child). In '95 we moved into our first office with three other team members, and it grew by about six team members every five years. With 21 full-time and four part-time, I would say that we have been careful to control our growth by doing a good job of forecasting and budgeting our overhead in order to have a healthy business, and to be able to pass on operational savings to our clients.

What geographic area do you serve?

We work all across North America; we've done business in 28 states, as well as planning for one of our university clients, which has a campus in Geneva, Switzerland. We are able to work long distance very efficiently because we began our careers working across the country, long distance with hospitals. That was back in the day when shipping in samples quickly was sending them overnight on a bus or an airplane, well before overnight FedEx and UPS.

What percentage of your business is healthcare?

Our work breaks down into three vertical markets:

- Healthcare: 50 percent
- Higher education: 30 percent
- Senior living: 20 percent—this is a big growth area

We actually see growth in all three of our markets, but as we all know, the baby boomers are getting older.

Do you refer to evidence-based art when helping a healthcare client come up with an art program?

Evidence-based design is certainly a buzzword these days; it is very exciting and progressive. I believe the whole language of evidence-based design was created in order to associate meaning to this movement of healthcare design as non-institutional in appearance, but still with patient safety/infection control, quality care/patient stress reduction, caregiver productivity, and of course environmental efficiencies.

However, many great designers were doing evidence-based work long before the term was invented. Evidence-based design is looking to create ways to measure what we do, and that is very important as the profession progresses.

Some research on evidence-based art suggests that abstract art is inappropriate for patient care areas. What is your opinion?

Hard abstraction, or pure abstraction (like Jackson Pollock) is difficult for many people to understand; they reject it. However, I do believe soft abstraction, with a component of realism, can work well in patient care areas, as long as the colors produce a sense of calmness. I am thinking patient care areas such as a chemotherapy infusion area where a patient needs to escape into an image that is thought provoking and calming at the same time. Truly, the general population does not like abstract, unless they can see imagery in it, such as mixed media collage artwork that has actual images within the overall piece. A large macro fine art photograph can have a sense of abstraction to it and still be very effective. What's fun in creating artwork master plans is to create an element of surprise and delight in key focal point areas.

What differentiates you from your competition in putting together art projects for hospitals?

Overall there are numerous artwork specialists around the country that can do a very good job of creating artwork in healthcare settings. I believe that my education and experience as an interior designer adds a huge benefit of integrating the art with the rest of the building architecture, interior design, and wayfinding. We design a lot of custom design features that incorporate art or become art. Our team has the resources and expertise to integrate these elements with the building that may require some architectural and/or engineering work by the design team or by the fabricator.

BUDGET

HOW TO SELL A HOSPITAL ART PROGRAM

Convincing a hospital CEO to invest in a hospital art program just got easier. Blair Sadler just published an article on the topic that should be required reading. Sadler is past president/CEO of Rady Children's Hospital in San Diego. He fully understands the perspective of hospital administrators—the people who make the decisions.

The article is titled, "The Business Case For Building Better Hospitals Through Evidence-Based Design." You can find it in the Spring 2008 issue of Health Environments Research and Design Journal.

This is a comprehensive article with more than 9,000 words. It deals with all aspects of evidence-based design, not just evidence-based art. However, the ideas are just the kind of ideas that show why it is worth investing in art.

The article listed 10 effective design interventions that are strongly supported by evidence. One of these is the appropriate use of art and music. Research shows that they reduce patient anxiety and stress and increase patient satisfaction. This is the crux of the argument for a hospital art program. Here is the abstract of the article:

Purpose: After establishing the connection between building well-designed evidence-based facilities and improved safety and quality for patients, families, and staff, this article presents the compelling business case for doing so. It demonstrates why ongoing operating savings and initial capital costs must be analyzed, and describes specific steps to ensure that design innovations are implemented effectively.

Background: Hospital leaders and boards are now beginning to face a new reality: They can no longer tolerate preventable hospital-acquired conditions such as infections, falls, and injuries to staff or unnecessary intra-hospital patient transfers that can increase errors. Nor can they subject patients and families to noisy, confusing environments that increase anxiety and stress. They must effectively deploy all reasonable quality improvement techniques available. To be optimally effective, a variety of tactics must be combined and implemented in an integrated way. Hospital leadership must understand the clear connection between building well-designed healing environments and improved healthcare safety and quality for patients, families, and staff, as well as the compelling business case for doing so. Emerging pay-for-performance methodologies that reward hospitals for quality and refuse to pay hospitals for the harm they cause (e.g., infections and falls) further strengthen this business case.

Recommendations: When planning to build a new hospital or to renovate an existing facility, healthcare leaders should address a key question: Will the proposed project incorporate all relevant and proven evidence-based design innovations to optimize patient safety, quality, and satisfaction, as well as workforce safety, satisfaction, productivity, and energy efficiency? When conducting a business case analysis for a new project, hospital leaders should consider ongoing operating savings and the market share impact of evidence-based design interventions, as well as initial capital costs. They should consider taking the 10 steps recommended to ensure an optimal, cost-effective hospital environment. A return-on-investment framework is put forward for the use of individual organizations.

The only way to read the article is to either subscribe to the magazine or buy a single copy. If you don't want to pay the $200 for the subscription, individual copies of the HERD Journal are available for $79 each. Customers may also order it by contacting the customer service department at 1-800-519-3692 or email customerservice@ vendomegrp.com.

SAVING MONEY—POSTER ART

Let me start with a confession: I have used poster art.

In 1993, when I was still practicing medicine, Christner Inc. designed a wonderful new medical building for me. As construction proceeded, we went over budget. When it came time to select art, we didn't give the designer, Beth Worthington (my sister), much of a budget. She had no choice but to select poster art.

Weaknesses of poster art
- Generic
- Less vivid
- Prints fade

Strengths of poster art
- Cheap

Eventually all the poster art was removed from my office walls and replaced with original nature prints. But many people who buy art from me are on a tight budget. A common solution I see is to put original "high quality" art in the more visible, public spaces. But for the back offices and patient rooms, poster art can help stretch the budget.

On-line sources of poster art:
- Bruce McGaw Graphics (www.bmcgaw.com)
- Bentley House (www.bentleypublishinggroup.com)
- Editions Limited (www.editionslimited.com)
- Galaxy of Graphics (www.galaxyofgraphics.com)

FUNDING HOSPITAL ART PROGRAMS

Art programs at hospitals often struggle for cash. A common approach to find that money is through a "foundation." These are independent, community-based charitable organizations that exist for the benefit of the hospital. They can help with fundraising from the local community.

In Jefferson City, Mo., where I used to work, Dianne Lowry is the development and foundation coordinator at St. Mary's Health Center. I asked her to share some ideas that might help others trying to raise money for art programs.

- Find patrons with a spiritual and emotional connection to art and to the facility.
- Have the foundation sponsor an event to highlight an artist. People who love art are used to art openings. This event can be a catalyst for support from the community.
- Have a gift acceptance policy in writing. If a donor offers you some valuable art, but the art does not fit with the hospital's art program, it will be clear that the art can be sold.

MOVING ART TO KEEP IT FRESH

How to get new art for free? Move what you have!

When I was still practicing medicine, we would move the 50 framed prints in my office once or twice a year. For months afterward, we would hear patients and staff talk about how much they liked the "new" art. But it was simply old art in a new location.

Most art in hospitals and offices (or your home!) will remain in the same position for years. As patients and staff become accustomed to images on a wall, they no longer see it.

A very inexpensive way to get new art is to move it around periodically; it keeps it fresh.

COMMENTS

We used to do this in retail, too—rearrange the merchandise

periodically. Inevitably customers would think we had new products, but all we had done was move things around.
Posted by: Cassie | May 21, 2007 at 03:00 AM

HOW TO SAVE THE ART BUDGET

My sister Beth, owner of Worthington Design in St. Louis, has been frustrated many times by having her art budget cut at the last minute when there are cost overruns. She voiced the concern of many when she suggested I discuss how to demonstrate to the CFO that "art matters"… so funding doesn't get cut or reallocated to capital equipment.

I asked designer Cindi Matras to offer her thoughts on this:

The key is to show how artwork can actually produce a return on investment. In my opinion, and from experience, there has to be a champion within a healthcare facility. Most frequently, this is not the CFO, as he or she may not see a direct financial correlation between cost to benefit. If the CEO or the officer in charge of 'facilities,' such as the CFO or COO, has an interest in the arts, an organization is more likely to be supportive of a successful arts program.

My approach is to first find that ally or champion within the organization who can help communicate the benefits (improving patient outcomes, relieving stress, creating a more patient-friendly environment, creating a more community-friendly space) to leadership.

The next step is piquing interest in community involvement in their facility by using the arts. I will usually offer the opportunity to utilize local scenes provided by local artists, which provides opportunities for the public to experience their facility in an alternative manner. Often leadership welcomes new ways for the public to 'see' their facilities instead of just a place to go when they or others they love are ill.

The next step is to introduce them to other opportunities for different types of art by discussing the creation of focal points within their facility that will encourage interaction, meditation, and wayfinding.

The fourth step is to create a vision. After a discussion of image and branding support, often I will send examples of artwork through email via Internet links, or will send real examples to the individuals I am targeting within the organization. This will help them see the potential and vision.

Providing a general budget and an estimate of the number of pieces it takes to accomplish the vision is the last step, and by that time, the client is usually convinced that this is something they should definitely include.

This does not work for all facilities, however. Urban sites have better access to the arts in general and understand the potential. It usually comes down to dollars, or lack of policy for managing artwork. Maintaining a focus on the public spaces for introducing limited, special pieces of art helps keep budget down, but creates a vision and sets the tone for a future program. These new programs can be introduced slowly and can be budgeted through capital improvement funds annually.

Cindi Matras is a registered interior designer in Wisconsin and currently acts as project development director and senior interior designer for Flad & Associates in Madison.

$250 MILLION YEARLY FOR ART

How much money is spent every year on art for healthcare?

I asked a leading expert, and she replied, "I have no idea what annual spending on healthcare art is . . . your guess is as good as mine!"

I could not find the numbers, but I did get estimates on the money spent on construction from page 2 of "Improving Healthcare with Better Building Design."

HealthCare construction spending in the United States is estimated to be $16.7 billion in 2005, rising to about $18.8 billion in 2009 (McGraw Hill Construction 2005) and to $33 billion by 2010 (Babwin 2002).

Let me make a rough guess on the percentage of the budget that is devoted to art. In Norway, it is supposed to be 1 percent. I would guess that in the United States, a quarter or an eighth of that is probably closer to the truth.

Understand that this is all a rough estimate, but I am trying to get a sense of the overall yearly budget.

If we assume healthcare construction is $20 billion per year, and we assume 1/8th of 1 percent (0.0125 percent) of that money will be devoted to art, then the math works like this: $20 trillion x 0.0125 percent = $250 million.

So perhaps $250 million to $500 million dollars is spent each year on art for healthcare in the United States. If anyone can give me more precise numbers, I would appreciate it.

How is this money spent? The bulk of it seems to go to many independent art consultants, interior design/architectural firms, mom-and-pop gallery shops, and a few national art consulting firms. A smaller percentage of the sales are from hospitals buying directly from artists.

SHOULD HOSPITALS SELL ART?

An article in the Wall Street Journal last week caught my eye. "Art Seller Helps Hotels Put on the Ritz," by Maneet Ahuja.

The idea is simple: Metropolitan Art Group offers to supply upscale hotels with fine-art prints to gussy up their rooms and common areas. The hotels can then sell copies of the prints to guests.

Would this model work in upscale hospitals? I could imagine the hospital having something like an "art cart" to let you pick what you want. Then, after living with it for a few days, you would really know if it is something you want to take home. You carry it with you as they push your wheelchair to be discharged. Try before you buy . . .

Because the hospitals would get a cut of the print sales, it might actually help a hospital's bottom line and sure to be popular with administration. Then there's prestige. Instead of the inexpensive poster art so common in patient rooms, this would be real art.

What do you think? Is this a good idea?

COMMENTS

When I go to a hospital, I want to heal. Art in the hospital sounds good. Maybe turning the pharmacy into a semi gift shop with a hard-bound book of prints and the like. But I would not want to see a price associated with the art on the wall. To me it would ruin the art experience.
Posted by: James | October 04, 2007 at 09:41 AM

James, I agree that seeing the price associated with the art would be horrible. But if you could pick the art you wanted on an "art cart," and you were supplied with a piece of paper explaining how you could buy the print, wouldn't that work?
Posted by: Henry Domke | October 05, 2007 at 07:28 AM

A brochure with contact info concerning availability of prints would be acceptable to me. I also think a coffee table book for waiting rooms would be a nice diversion for the people using the rooms
Posted by: James | October 05, 2007 at 03:32 PM

BARGAIN PAINTINGS FROM CHINA

Oil paintings are usually too expensive to fit into the budget of a new hospital. It helps if you have a donor who would give one from their collection. Now there is another way to have real oil paintings: have them made in China.

To learn in more detail about how this works, I interviewed Wujie Li. He owns The Oil Painting Studio.

Tell me about how The Oil Painting Studio got started. When did it form? How many people work there? How many artists? What city is it in?
The website was founded in 2001, but we started the oil paintings

business before that. First I worked for the biggest gallery in the Netherlands as an oil painter. Since I was working harder than the other Chinese, after a year, the gallery gave me all of the orders in China. But I couldn't do them all by myself, so I created the studio. I found more good artists and trained them to fill the orders requested. Now there are 22 artists in the studio. We are located in the middle of China in Jiaozuo.

If an art consultant in the United States wanted to have a particular painting made, could they send you a reproduction of the painting that you or one of the other artists there could use as a template?
Yes, this is our work every day. The clients can send us the picture or image by email. We do the paintings according to clients' requests.

How does payment work? If an art consultant wanted to have you make 10 paintings, do they have to give you a down payment? Do you take credit cards?
Usually if the client places an order, they need to send half the money first, and then we start the painting. When the painting is finished, we will send the client an image for approval. If it is acceptable, the client makes the rest of the payment. If not, we will make changes until the client is satisfied. We accept payment by PayPal, wire, and Western Union.

How is the art shipped? Can you use FedEx?
We use FedEx, DHL, and UPS.

I would assume that one of the reasons someone in America would go to the trouble of working with you is that your prices are much better. Can you give me examples of prices?
Our prices are as follows:

12"–16" = $160	24"–30" = $340
16"–20" = $200	24"–36" = $360
20"–24" = $240	30"–40" = $420
20"–30" = $300	36"–48" = $480

Prices do not including shipping and framing. We create quality top-notch, realistic paintings.

Is there anything else you would like to say?

I have been in the business for more than 12 years, and I am not only the boss, but also an artist. So I know what service is required and what the United States painting market is like. I have others clients in the United States. For example, one of them is a businessman who likes horses, so he orders horse paintings for horse shows, which he then sells...very interesting...

For more information, go to www.oilpaintingstudio.com.

WOULD UNIVERSAL HEALTHCARE MEAN NO ART?

There is a boom in healthcare construction in the United States that has resulted in a surge of demand for healthcare art. What would happen to the healthcare art market if political forces brought us universal healthcare?

My best guess: universal healthcare would cause no change in the high demand for healthcare art or healthcare construction.

If you look at countries that offer universal health coverage (which includes every developed nation on earth except the United States), you will see that they continue to fund the purchase of art for healthcare. Some countries like Norway require that 1 percent of the construction cost be spent on art.

The idea for this post was triggered when reading this week's New England Journal of Medicine. The lead article is titled, "Coverage for All Americans." They write:

> Since 47 million Americans lack health insurance and many others have inadequate coverage, we wanted to explore how the presidential candidates propose to provide healthcare for all Americans while controlling costs and maintaining quality.

BASIC ADVICE ON HOSPITAL ART PROGRAMS

I asked art consultant Peppe Dragoni, president of Ground Zero Designs, to share some tips on the most effective ways a hospital can save money on art programs. She has 20 years experience in the field and has worked with more than 1,500 clients. I found it interesting that she focused on setting a comfortable mood and avoiding abstract, frightening, or ambiguous images. Her experience in the field supports what researcher Roger Ulrich has found.

Key things to do:
- Try to make everyone "somewhat happy"
- Make it simple and pretty
- Set a mood for a calming environment
- Try to keep it warm, colorful, friendly, inviting, and most of all, comforting

Key things to avoid:
- No abstracts
- No large blotches of color without shape or reality
- No vacant chairs, no leafless trees, no lonely beaches
- No scary images, no teeth
- No blurry or out-of-focus images
- No political or racial blurbs
- No subliminal behavior modification

BUYING ART FOR HOSPITALS ON EBAY

Poster art is a widely used way to put up pictures in a hospital without breaking the budget. Posters are mass produced on cheap paper to keep down cost. The colors may not be as vivid, and it certainly won't be archival, but they are cheap. The trouble is that poster art looks cheap.

What if you want real art—original art—on a tight budget?

One option is to look to China. But that takes a long time and may involve having to trust someone on the other side of the planet who is not fluent in English.

Another option is to use eBay.

I just checked and there are 234,175 pieces of art on eBay right now. They are conveniently arranged into three categories

- Direct from the artist
- Art from dealers and resellers
- Wholesale lots

I've seen three examples of art on eBay recently. One was an entire room in a gallery filled with paintings from eBay. Another is a distinguished painting professor who sells his watercolors on eBay, rather than have them sit in storage. Lastly, I know a photographer who sells his platinum prints on eBay for as little as $25.

I'm certain you can find some real bargains for original art on eBay. A serious problem with this method is that it takes too much time. I suspect that most art buyers for hospitals won't take the time or risk getting involved with buying art on eBay.

RESOURCES

| HOW TO START A HOSPITAL ART PROGRAM |

Suzanne Randolph, an independent art advisor, presented one of the four talks on "How to Start a Visual Arts Program in a Healthcare Setting" today. This was the beginning of the symposium on "The Importance and Value of Art in Healthcare" at the Museum of Modern Art in New York.

I thought Randolph had some practical advice that might be helpful to others. Here are my condensed notes:

Step 1: Define the scope of the project
- Who is the audience?
- What is appropriate for that audience?
- Where can you place the art to get the biggest bang for the buck?
- What is the budget and timetable?
  Key idea: Be flexible

Step 2: Where do you find the art?
- Galleries and unaffiliated artists
- Artist registries
- Schools
- Not-for-profit arts organizations
- Patient-created art

Step 3: Who makes it happen?
- Dedicated staff or, if possible, an arts administrator
- Independent art advisors
- Volunteer advisory committees
  Key to success: Collaboration

Randolph is an independent art advisor with 25 years of experience. She is based in New York City. Randolph's website is www.suzannerandolphfinearts.com.

The conference was jointly sponsored by the Office of Cultural Enrichment at Vanderbilt University Medical Center, the Society for the Arts in Healthcare, and the Museum of Modern Art.

BLAIR SADLER'S 10 RULES FOR HEALTHCARE ART PROJECTS

Blair Sadler gave one of the best talks at the symposium on "The Importance and Value of Art in Healthcare" held at the Museum of Modern Art. First, he gave an inspirational tour of some innovative art programs that have won the Healing Arts Award.

He went on to give some very practical advice on how to win the support of hospital administrators for arts projects. He can speak with authority on this since he was the CEO of a large hospital for many years; he knows the concerns of hospital administrators.

Sadler's 10 rules for adding value to healthcare organizations through the arts are:

- Do your homework. Understand your clients' strategic, operational, and financial realities.
- Begin with a sure success project—one with a high likelihood of visible and widespread impact.
- Make a compelling case. Describe how the project will help your client win in their market.
- Find effective champions. Seek credible internal advocates who will support the project.

- Secure funding from new sources. Find art (not healthcare) donors.
- Understand the emerging new evidence and decide what is relevant to your project.
- Commit to research. Collaborate with your client to develop pre-project baseline measures. Measure the impact on patients, families, employees, volunteers, or donors.
- Provide regular progress reports. Include key leaders and donors.
- Meet your deadlines and budget. No exceptions, no excuses.
- Share the credit with your client and publish your results.

NONPROFITS PLACING ART IN HOSPITALS

Elaine Poggi sent me information on four friends of hers who have created nonprofit organizations dedicated to placing art in hospitals.

- John Feight, The Foundation for Hospital Art. Poggi says, "I'm sure you must know of this organization. I have helped paint in one of their paintfests in a hospital in Florence. They do great work!"
- Ken Sexton, The Hospital Art Foundation. Poggi says, "He lives in Canada and places any kind of artwork from anyone who wants to donate in hospitals in Canada. He is a businessman who just wanted to make hospitals nicer!"
- Kate Strasburg, Healing Environments. Poggi says, "She and her friend Traci have done great work in creating healing environments and choosing art for these projects. They also produce a wonderful journal called 'A Light in the Mist' and send it to hospitals all over the world."
- Amy Camie, Scientific Arts Foundation. Poggi says, "She is a harpist and is working on research with harp music in hospitals."

Elaine Poggi founded and heads The Foundation for Photo/Art in Hospitals, a nonprofit, publicly supported organization dedicated to placing comforting nature art in hospital world-wide.

ART CORNER – SHOWCASING HEALTHCARE ARTISTS

If you are an interior designer, architect, or art consultant, how do you find new art?

If you are an artist who wants to have your work in a healthcare environment, how do you find new customers?

One answer is the monthly column, "Art Corner," that is in Healthcare Design magazine. This is a one- or two-page article featuring an individual artist. There are always high-quality color photographs to show the work in various healthcare facilities.

Editor Richard Peck started the column in 2003, and it has been in every regular issue since then. Peck answered a few questions about the column:

How does an artist get to be featured in Art Corner?

The easiest way for an artist to get in is to send a press kit we can review, or at least inform us in some way that's intriguing. Once in a while, though, we'll see something in another venue (website, conference) that looks interesting.

Can artists contact you directly to ask for consideration?

Yes, we're always open to contacts, and the best approach is an email with attachments (with the art in low-res so as to not slow up things; we can ask for hi-res later).

What is the history of Art Corner? Who thought of it? How has it evolved?

I guess Art Corner was my brainchild. I've always been interested in how artists make things, and our original number involved these sculptural sails that were used as space-dividers in a naval hospital. We have since presented a variety of sculptures, giant mobiles, etched glass, water features, fine art, and even a nature photographer whose name escapes me. (Note: Richard Peck wrote an article on my work for the May 2005 Art Corner. Art Corner inspired me to do the featured artist column on this blog.) We also had fun covering the installation of a giant, sculpted 'tree' at MD Anderson in Houston.

Who picks the artists for Art Corner?

I have picked the artists for the most part, though managing editor Todd Hutlock has become more involved in this of late. He is actually running the department now.

NEOCON

This post is NOT about the political movement that emerged as a rejection of liberalism and the counter-culture of the 1960s. However, that is what turned up when I searched for "NeoCon" on Wikipedia.

The NeoCon that I am referring to is the "National Exposition of Contract Furnishings." It is a big event; more than 50,000 designers and 1,200 showrooms. I asked an experienced designer (Cindi Matras) who has been to NeoCon several times to introduce the topic:

> NeoCon takes place annually in Chicago at the Merchandise Mart. The show focuses on rolling out the new products that commercial interior designers might use on a project. Products include furniture, flooring, wallcovering, lighting, sustainable design products and sometimes artwork.
>
> One can see a variety of art exhibited there; however, the focus is most consistently on artwork for use in architecture, such as metal art, glass for either sculptural features or a specialty wall or piece of furniture. I have, on occasion, seen other forms of wall art exhibited. Most often, there are dealers present who work with a variety of artists to sell limited edition prints, poster art, and sometimes sculpture and commissioned works. Sometimes there are dealers who present new software that show many artists' works on line.
>
> It is a fun experience, and the building is quite 'abuzz' with designers dressed in the latest fashions, discussing the latest products. The energy is great, but be prepared to walk a lot!

Cindi Matras is a registered interior designer in Wisconsin and currently acts as project development director and senior interior designer for Flad & Associates in Madison. She has extensive health-care design experience and more than 20 years of experience procuring artwork for healthcare, corporate, academic and municipal facilities.

DESIGN LIBRARIES

As I started to visit interior design firms and architectural offices, I noticed that most had design libraries. I wasn't sure how they worked or how they might be used to select art, so I asked Cindi Matras, an experienced designer, to explain them to me.

What are design libraries for? What sorts of things are stored in them?
Design libraries are a compilation of resources, product catalogs and samples of products that are useful for architects and design-ers when specifying building and construction materials, finishes, and artwork. A typical library would contain Sweets Catalogs, which is sort of a large condensed catalog of many manufacturers in one book . . . a sort of 'encyclopedia of products.' Also contained in the library would be various product catalogs that include all the differ-ent product offerings a manufacturer has, plus the specifications of the product. If the library is sizeable, it will often contain samples of miscellaneous building and interior products that show size, color, texture, and quality of a particular material.

Artwork is one type of product that may be seen in a design library. Our library at Flad, for example, contains catalogs provided by various art dealers of posters, prints, and limited edition artwork. We also use our library to showcase specific pieces of art, such as your portfolio of prints, or CDs of other's artwork.

Are design libraries a good way to find art for healthcare? How does that work?
Design libraries are a very good place to start. Artists are now provid-ing CDs of their art, which is very easy to store and update. It is also very convenient for the designer/architect.

I always recommend meeting with the artist face to face, or with the dealer if you are specifying specialty pieces of art; especially when it comes to art for healthcare. Since art in the healthcare environment is usually a very sensitive issue, it is always best to make certain you know what you are getting and are not basing your decisions on a color image. Caveat to this . . . unless the artist is providing high-res images that are very representative of their work, similar to what you provide with your work.

How common are design libraries? Are they just at big firms?

Design libraries are very common, and most design professionals would deem them a necessary tool to do their work. The size and amount of material within each library is very dependent on the size of the firm and how much real estate is available. Often times, a small firm or a one-owner firm may 'rent' or use another firm's library. Co-op libraries are becoming more common as several smaller firms may share office space or adjacent tenant spaces.

Is there always a librarian? What does the librarian do?

It is not very common to have a resource librarian for the small to average design firm. Often, a design or architectural intern will manage the resources as part of their position, or potentially, the responsibilities will be shared between employees. The advantage to having a librarian is that time is not taken away from project time by a 'chargeable' or 'billable' staff person. Also, the librarian can become very familiar with products and act as a 'one-stop shopping' resource for the design and architectural staff. Many of the large firms have librarians, or are moving in the direction. For a designer, it is definitely considered a perk and is sometimes a recruiting tool for bringing in and retaining staff.

How has the Internet changed the way design libraries are used?

Manufacturers are now changing the way they do business due to the Internet, and I can't say I blame them. Many are going to electronic catalogs, which are very easily accessible by anyone. It is also a very cost-effective way to manage their clients—the architects and designers. Instead of having to print a new catalog or binder for each design/architectural library, each time they have a price increase, or a product change, they are now able to make a change on the net, with very little distribution cost. Internet access to products is very convenient. However, many manufacturers aren't quite there yet and, even if they are, don't offer all their product, or images of their product on the net.

TIPS ON PICKING SCULPTURE

Sculpture is widely used in the lobbies and entrances to hospitals.

What should you look for when picking sculpture for healthcare?

Since my background is in photography and painting, I thought I would ask someone else. I met Stacey Lindell at the Healthcare Design 06 conference. She is artistic manager for Clowes Sculpture in New Hampshire, and I found her to be remarkably articulate. Since she works with sculpture, I asked her to share a few thoughts:

It is critical that our artwork be soothing, inspiring, and set the stage for a healing environment. The three things that I feel are important are:
- Scale
- Materials
- Clientele

The scale of the artwork must integrate well with the architecture. If it is too small or large, it simply will not harmonize with the environment. It could be perceived negatively by patients and particularly by the staff. Careful proportioning will allow the audience to relate and interact with the work.

The materials for the work must be high quality, interesting in detail, suit the ambiance of the interior, but most importantly, be durable and easily cleaned. The artwork must not be a welcome host to germs or mold.

Finally, careful consideration of the type of patients should be a deciding factor for the sculpture. I would not place a flower sculpture in a hospital or center that specialized in prostate cancer. Finding a balance and harmony with the mission of the facility is very important. This provides buy-in from staff and patients alike.

Attention to these three factors will likely yield a work of art that is comforting, interesting, and valued by the facility and its clients. The artwork can function as an important branding icon for the facility and be a positive investment for the hospital and community.

AMERICAN ART RESOURCES TOUR

This week I was lucky enough to tour American Art Resources in Houston. It is the largest company providing art for healthcare in North America.

Key impression: This is a powerful way to deliver art for healthcare.

Observations:

- They are a full-service company that works out of two adjacent buildings on a quiet, tree-lined street in Houston. Currently they employ 31 people.
- They do everything from early planning for an art program to actually delivering and installing the art anywhere in America.
- They were a pioneer in exploring evidence-based art, and remain a leader in the field by employing a full-time researcher, Dr. Upali Nanda.
- They have been remarkably innovative at improving efficiency in every step of the process. This is true from having their own custom database to process and track every step and piece of complex orders, to the layout of the frame shop to reduce the number of steps needed to move a print along the framing process.
- They (and their customers) benefit from the economics of scale

and specialization. Given their large size they can get quantity pricing not available to smaller companies.

- Eight of their staff are "consultants" (actually interior designers or architects) that help with art selection and layout. Three staff members are dedicated installers. In the frame shop, different people specialize in different parts of the job. For example, one person is in charge of cutting mats and another for cutting glass.

To learn more about American Art Resources, visit the website www.americanartresources.com.

WHAT IT MEANS TO BE ARCHIVAL

Archival is simply the ability of something to last for many years. Given enough time, all things will deteriorate because entropy rules. This sad fact is explained by the Second Law of Thermodynamics.

How long prints have to last before they can be considered archival is debatable. As a general rule, prints can be called archival if they show no perceptible change over 100 years, assuming they will be kept away from prolonged periods of direct sunlight.

Direct sunlight can be very damaging to any art. We think of oil paintings as something that will endure for centuries, but if they are exposed to harsh conditions, paintings can fade much quicker.

I made a copy of a Van Gogh's "Portrait of a Man with a Skull Cap" in oil more than a decade ago for practice when I was in art school. Because it had no value, I thought it would be interesting to see how it would tolerate the elements, so I nailed it to the south side of our barn, fully exposed to the sun. Now, after 10 years, it has faded considerably.

So what can you do in a healthcare setting to assure your prints won't fade?

- Insist that the art you buy is made with archival methods (pigment-based ink, acid-free paper).

- Make sure your art is not exposed to direct sunlight.
- Use some form of UV protection (UV glass and/or a protective varnish).

SOCIETY FOR THE ARTS IN HEALTHCARE

Designers and art consultants kept telling me, "You should join the Society for the Arts in Healthcare." So I went to the website, looked around, and decided it was worth the $125 membership fee.

To learn more, I asked the staff at their headquarters in Washington, D.C., a few questions.

What is the primary purpose of the Society for the Arts in Healthcare?

The Society for the Arts in Healthcare promotes the use of the arts as an essential part of healthcare. We educate about the valuable role the arts can play in the healing process and help individuals and organizations build and strengthen programs through education, resources and consulting services.

How does it relate to the other nonprofit organizations involved with healthcare design? Complementary? Competition? Different angle?

SAH is the only U.S.-based national not-for-profit organization exclusively dedicated to ensuring access to the visual, literary, and performing arts and design in all healthcare experiences.

How many people are in the Society for the Arts in Healthcare? Who are they?

We have nearly 1,700 members worldwide. Our members include people from many walks of life. We have artists, designers, architects, healthcare providers, hospital administrators, researchers, educators, and many others.

How can you help artists, interior designers, and hospital staff?

We offer programs, educational and networking opportunities, and consulting services to the field.

With our on-line and printed publications we offer information about model programs, best practices and cutting-edge arts in healthcare research.

We also publish job and volunteer opportunities, recent news articles, and member news and announcements.

Do you have any conferences or events?
We have an annual conference, as well as regional meetings throughout the United States and Canada. To learn more, go to www.thesah. org and click on 'events.'

Anything else you would like to say?
We have a unique grant initiative. For six years, Johnson & Johnson, in partnership with the Society for the Arts in Healthcare, has provided funding for programs in the United States and Canada, which serve as models for improving healthcare through the use of arts.

The staff members who answered these questions were Anita Boles, executive director; Sarah Kemp, programs director; and Evlyn Baker, operations manager.

HOW TO WORK WITH AN ART CONSULTANT

As I started to focus on providing art for healthcare, I quickly realized that much of the art is selected by art consultants. To learn more about them, I interviewed Barbara Harriman, who is an art consultant and president of Distinctive Art Resources.

Why would an interior designer subcontract the art selection and installation to an art consultant?
Art consultants can become strong allies with project architects and designers. By selecting an art consultant, designers and architects are able to provide design direction to the art program without expending costly production hours.

Art consultants have vast artist resource libraries and connections with art communities, which allow them to offer a wide variety of selections/solutions in minimal amounts of time. Art consultants' expertise, paired with their resources, can result in saving the client time and additional fees while providing creative art options and solutions.

Turnkey art consultants also provide the luxury of using one source for all art needs, including installation.

What percentage of your work is for interior designers/architects?
30 percent.

What percentage is for facility owners?
70 percent.

How does one find an art consultant?
It is the art consultant's job to help facilities create an art program that surpasses their expectations, so an art consultant should be chosen based on ability to offer creative suggestions and solutions while remaining within budget and on schedule.

Facilities and architects/designers should look for an art consultant who actively seeks direction from the facility (art committee) and the design team, as both have been integrally involved in the project long before the art consultant's arrival.

Other criteria to consider when choosing an art consultant:

- Do they work only in healthcare?
- Do they select art based on research-informed decisions so as to mitigate stress and offer the possibility of improved patient outcomes?
- Do they have a history of completing art programs on time and within budget?
- Is their pricing competitive?
- Do they charge consulting fees?
- What do past clients say about working with them?

For healthcare projects, is it important to find someone who specializes in art for healthcare?

Absolutely, as art can not only enhance healing environments, but also integrate with marketing strategies by becoming the visual face of a facility.

What percent of your work is healthcare?

100 percent.

Any suggestions on how to best work with an art consultant?

Contact an art consultant early on in the project for budget information. Even if it is not time to begin developing the art program, an art consultant can help define realistic budgets as early as the design development phase.

Or, once you are ready to begin working on the art portion of a project, contact the art consultant to discuss process as well as the project's scope, style, interior finishes, and expected completion date. The art consultant can then provide you with a suggested project timeline and additional budget information.

How are art consultants paid? Per hour or a percentage of sales?

This varies between art consultants. I can only speak for Distinctive Art Source. Typically, there are no art consulting fees involved with our services. Our costs are covered in the price of purchased art. Due to our high purchase volume, we are able to pass considerable savings on to facilities. Should a facility request specific services (such as an art inventory, call for artists, or creation of a community art gallery), we will provide a proposal for the requested services with minimum and maximum fees defined.

Original or commissioned art is often sold at cost plus a percentage or at cost plus an hourly fee (for time spent finding and commissioning the artist).

Anything else you would like to add?

A healthcare art program is successful when positive responses are optimized, stress is mitigated, wayfinding is enhanced, goals are achieved, budgets remain intact, and expectations are surpassed.

Could you tell me a little about your art consulting business?

Distinctive Art Source, a national art consulting firm, works exclusively in healthcare. While our focus is creating patient-based art programs (centered on research and owner/architect/designer input), our goals are two-fold: to bring unexpected art options and solutions to each project and to involve the local art community whenever possible. Our firm's architectural background is structured to blend seamlessly into the design process providing owners with necessary budgets and timelines right from the start. Budget and schedule are important to us; we do not exceed budgets and we do not miss deadlines.

To learn more about Distinctive Art Resources, visit the website www.distinctiveartsource.com.

CALIBRATE YOUR MONITOR TO GET COLORS RIGHT

I encourage customers to let me send them free sample prints of images they are considering. That way they can be sure the color is correct. I have to keep reminding them that the color on their computer monitors is inaccurate. That is because 99 percent of computer monitors in the world are not calibrated.

If you want to do one thing to improve the color accuracy of your work on the computer, I suggest calibrating your monitor. It ALWAYS helps. You can buy the equipment needed to do it for under $100. For example, you can buy the ColorVision Spyder2 Express for only $80.

It is very easy to use. Simply plug it in, specify your display type, and it does the rest, automatically calibrating your monitor or laptop. When I check the "before" and "after," I am always impressed with the difference it makes.

If you are care about color, you owe it to yourself to get your monitor calibrated.

COMMENTS

Henry, I just calibrated my computer with ColorVision. There is a difference!! Thanks for the tip!

Posted by: Elaine Poggi | October 13, 2007 at 02:16 PM

BLAIR SADLER'S HEALING ARTS AWARDS

The purpose of the awards is to recognize artists that have had a measurable impact on the healthcare experience. Awards range from $500 to $1,000.

Types of art:
• Literary
• Visual
• Performing
• Multidisciplinary
• Media arts projects

The awards can go to individuals or teams of individuals. There are awards for professionals and students.

Blair L. Sadler, J.D., is the vice chair of the board of directors of The Center for Health Design. Among his many achievements, he is known for his presentations where he explains the business case for building optimal hospitals.

Annette Ridenour, president of Aesthetics, Inc., is a co-founder of the Blair Sadler Awards. Aesthetics, Inc. is the administrator for the competition and awards program.

Applicants must be members of the Society for the Arts in Healthcare. The competition has been a partnership with the Society for the Arts in Healthcare since its inception in 2001.

FINDING LOCAL ART

An art consultant I work with emailed me yesterday:

'I'm looking for abstract/contemporary photography of sites and buildings throughout San Bernardino County; do you have any images from there? If not, can you refer me to someone?"

Many clients ask for art that is specific to a given location. How do you find that? The Internet plays a central role. Here are some possible ways to find site specific art.

- Do a Google search — Enter the location and what you are looking for, such as "San Bernardino" and "landscape photographs."
- Call art schools in the vicinity you are interested in. If you want paintings, ask to speak to one of the painting professors.
- Contact local galleries — Many communities have art leagues that know the art of emerging and local artists.

AMERICAN ACADEMY OF HEALTHCARE INTERIOR DESIGNERS

This week Jocelyn Stroupe, IIDA, AAHID, asked if I would like to join AAHID as a sponsor. Stroupe is the director of healthcare interiors at OWP/P and serves on the AAHID board of regents. I only had a vague idea about what the organization was about, so I asked Peter Brooks, their executive director, a few questions.

Who joins the AAHID?

The people who join AAHID are really passionate and dedicated to creating healing environments for people. Specifically, these are interior designers who specialize in healthcare to assure their clients they are qualified, knowledgeable, and have expertise. The client can be sure they are hiring a designer who has experience in healthcare and has been tested, certified, and endorsed by the academy.

What is involved with becoming a "certificant?"

It really starts with the NCIDQ certification. That is the minimum professional certification in design. For AAHID certification, the designer must have worked within healthcare for five years. They fill out an application, send us a portfolio, and are invited to sit for a four-hour exam, which they must pass. The certificants are seasoned veterans in healthcare design.

Are certificants required to understand how to use art in healthcare?

Absolutely. Art is one of the major components of evidence-based design. We have strong proof of the value of art and it is not only a positive distraction that reduces stress, but it is also therapeutic. Roger Ulrich, Ph.D., has provided probably the greatest substantiated body of research that proves the value of art in healthcare, and there are questions on the exam regarding art in healthcare.

How are they tested on the use of art in healthcare?

Students are tested in the following areas: acute care, ambulatory care/outpatient, long-term care/senior living, medical facilities/other, retail/hospitality, support services, allied professions, codes and guidelines, environmental, evidence-based design, and professional business practice. Art as therapy and distraction are included in the environment and evidence-based design sections.

Is there anything else you would like to say about the AAHID?

Our vision is to become the single source for the healthcare interior design professional. To that end, we are looking to provide research, evaluations, plans, presentations, scholarships, and mentoring opportunities to our design, healthcare, and industry partners. The academy is working to cultivate and disseminate best practices within the profession. To partner, volunteer, and support the academy is an excellent opportunity to network, learn and hold up these professionals who are committed to doing what they can to help people in need. AAHID is a certified 501(c)3 organization; our website is www.aahid.org.

After thinking about it, I did apply to become an industry partner.

CENTER FOR THE ARTS IN HEALTHCARE RESEARCH & EDUCATION

The names of some organizations are just too long; too much of a mouthful. Try saying, "The Center for the Arts in Healthcare Research & Education." It just does not roll off the tongue easily. So it is abbreviated as "CAHRE." But even that is awkward.

A better name would be "Florida Healthcare Art."

They study the effects of art in healthcare settings in Florida. They also have an educational component to help train others how to best use art in hospitals. The educational part of their work has a global reach, with a variety of projects in Africa.

CAHRE was started in 1999 following the establishment of the nation's first university-level coursework in the arts in healthcare. The center grew from the groundbreaking clinical work of the Shands Arts in Medicine program. In their first decade, they have grown to be one of the leaders in the field.

They established the first on-line database on research in the use of art in healthcare. This database is now hosted on the Society for Arts in Healthcare website. For more information, visit their website at www.arts.ufl.edu/cahre.

FINDING A STONE CARVER

Stone carving is one of the most ancient and durable of all art forms. Having a stone sculpture prominently placed near the entrance of a hospital can help create an atmosphere suggesting longevity and quality. How do architects, designers, and art consultants find stone sculptors and stone art for their projects? I don't have any experience with this at all, so I asked an artist friend, Bill Knight.

> As one who is primarily a private or hobby artist, I lack direct experience about how these things work, so I don't have a good answer for you. I can tell you, though, how I have found stone sculpture to study and enjoy, and that has been through the Internet. You might say I have too much time on my hands, but I have spent hundreds of hours ferreting out stonework.
>
> A very common way for a town or city to boost its cultural profile and enrich itself with art is to hold a stone-carving symposium. Participating sculptors are selected on the basis of their

portfolio or a proposal maquette (a small model). Very good records of these events are kept on-line, and they feature photographs and artists' resumes which, in turn, offer links to more symposia or artists' websites. Another avenue I have taken is the obvious one of Googling search words related to stone sculpture, stone types, and names of carvers once I know them.

Using geographic signifiers such as town or nationality can be very helpful, especially when the search words are in the language of the nation. Japan has an amazingly vibrant granite carving scene with many, many symposia and artists. Googling in English has had great results, though I have had to be very patient working my way though sites where I could not read the text. Cutting and pasting the Japanese characters of artists' names also produces good results.

For people not wanting to go to these lengths, I can recommend three websites that maintain stone sculptor lists and links:

- The Stone Foundation (www.stonefoundation.org)
- Stone Carvers Guild (www.stonecarversguild.com)
- About Stone Directory (www.AboutStone.org)

About Stone has hundreds of artists and their websites listed and is by far the most comprehensive, but its size also makes it difficult to use. It is not easy to get a quick idea of the artwork without actually visiting each site, and much of it is not professional or public.

The question of how to find great artists not mentioned on those sites remains. It's beyond my ken, but I conjecture that a need for a consultant/panel of peers remains. I could try to help if people wanted to email me.

Knight trained as a stone carver during his studies at Washington University's art school in St. Louis. He lives on a farm near Fredericktown, Mo., with his wife Angela, who is also an artist.

HCD08 – BEST HEALTHCARE DESIGN CONFERENCE

I only go to one conference a year, so I want to make sure it is the best. The healthcare design conference (this year called HEALTH-CARE DESIGN 08 or HCD08) is what I'm looking for. This will be the fourth year in a row that I have exhibited there. The only change I would like to see is a broader international presence.

The very best people in the field are there—the decision-makers, the best designers, the top organizations, and the most progressive facilities.

It is also the best place to learn about and see art for healthcare. The top providers of art for healthcare have a major presence. Glancing at a list of exhibitors, I found:

- American Art Resources
- Art Dallas Incorporated
- Art.com
- Artline Wholesalers
- Distinctive Art Source
- Health Environment Art Services
- Henry Domke Fine Art
- Meltdown Glass Art & Design LLC
- Monte Nagler Photography, LLC
- Murals Your Way
- PI Fine Art
- Sky Factory (The)
- Skyline Art Company
- Skyline Design
- Spellman Brady & Company

WHY I WON'T BE GOING TO THE SAH CONFERENCE

"SAH" is the abbreviation for the "Society for Arts in Healthcare."

Last week, a reader wrote, "If you are an artist in this field, do you recommend going to the SAH Conference?"

Since she is a visual artist, I did not recommend the conference. SAH seems to be preoccupied with performance art: poetry, theater, dance, and music. In my opinion, these play a minor role in most hospitals. Greater emphasis should be given to the visual arts.

Today in the mail I got the brochure for the 20th SAH conference to be held this April in Buffalo. A quick glance at the 61 events showed only five that clearly deal with visual art.

Two of the talks particularly appeal to me:

- The effect of art on patient stress in psychiatric units, by Dr. Sarajane Eisen-Brown
- Different approaches to research on children's art preferences, by Dr. Upali Nanda

But as excellent as those talks are sure to be, it is not enough for me to justify taking three days out of my work week and spending $1,000 (conference, room and board, plus travel). Since I am a visual artist, I don't want to spend the time and money at a conference where the focus is on performance art.

Annette Ridenour was on the board of SAH since the beginning and served as its president for two terms. When I interviewed her about the SAH conference last year, she said, "I believe that SAH should be spending more time on the visual arts and less time on performance arts." Ridenour runs one of the largest companies involved with art in healthcare, Aesthetics Inc. (www.aesthetics.net).

Perhaps the conference will be right for you. If you are a music therapist or are involved in art therapy, there are many programs that might interest you. To learn more the SAH, go to www.thesah.org.

FRAMING

CONTROLLING FRAMING COSTS

When I started to have gallery exhibits, I learned quickly how expensive framing is. Many people spend as much on framing as they do on the art itself.

For suggestions on how to save on framing, I talked to Puneet Bhasin. Bhasin is vice president at Artline, a contract framer with offices in New York, Florida, Illinois, and California.

He suggested that designers:

- Specify consistent image sizes
- Use a wholesale frame shop
- Install it themselves
- Use regular Plexiglas instead of non-glare
- Use the same molding throughout the facility

Why is consistent image size so important? "This enables the framers to purchase material pre-cut (i.e., mats, foamcore, and Plexiglas). Doing so keeps the labor cost lower, rather than having assorted sizes and having the machines readjusted for different sizes. Another idea is to use as few molding styles as possible. This has two advantages: It brings the design together, so all the frames are consistent, and it gives buying power to the framer to purchase molding in bulk."

What misperception do people have about wholesale frame shops?

"The most common misperception is that they are saving money by having the framing done locally. Most local frame shops charge close to double the price Artline offers."

GLAZING TIPS

Jan Marion, owner of H. Marion Framing Studio in Glenview, Ill., has a lot of experience framing art in healthcare. I asked him to give me a few tips on glazing.

Let's start with a definition of glazing—panes or sheets of glass or acrylic set or made to be set in frames, as in windows, doors, or mirrors. In the art world, glazing material will protect art and provide protection from dust and dirt, abrasion, and in some cases, ultra violet radiation and glare issues. All works of art on paper should be protected with glazing.

Typically, an inkjet print on canvas, or original oil or acrylic painting on canvas, does not require glazing. However, in some high traffic environments, the added protection is advisable.

Use of glass vs. acrylic—there are pros and cons for each. Glass is twice as heavy as acrylic, so anything larger than roughly 32" x 40" should be glazed using acrylic.

Use of a very small or fragile frame might require the lighter acrylic glazing material. There are many types of non-glass glazing options. Acrylic in sheet form has the best optical clarity and should be the only choice for the picture framing industry.

Various thicknesses are available: 1/8" should accommodate most projects. 3/16" or 1/4" should be used for larger projects, or in situations where sagging could be an issue (i.e., huge works or shadow box designs where the acrylic is not supported by a mat). Acrylic will scratch easier than glass. Acrylic is available in non-glare, UV-filtering, and abrasion resistance (resists scratches and chemicals).

Non-glare will eliminate glare, but introduces some distortion. Non-glare is beneficial when designing nursing homes. Sclerosis of the lenses, cataracts, and strokes often lead to vision problems. To eliminate glare, a non-glare glass or acrylic is important. Be mindful that the non-glare finish will dull the colors slightly, so select imagery with brighter colors to offset this factor.

If you want no glare and no distortion, then museum glass is the product for you. In a healthcare application, however, this may not be practical. It may be cost prohibitive, but more importantly, it is difficult to work with and not practical to maintain on site.

If budgets are tight? Glass is less expensive and preferred for its low maintenance properties. Special (thinner) 2mm glass is also available, but it can break easier.

As a personal aside, I would like to mention the option of not using glazing. I realize that in healthcare settings this is not an option, but in homes, I think it should be considered. At my house, we never put glass over my inkjet prints. Even in my gallery exhibitions I skip glass. Not once have I had a print damaged, and since I use archival inks, the UV protection of glass is less important. The key advantage of no glazing is no glare and no optical distortion; and of course, it is cheaper...

My wife Lorna likes to say, "Putting glass in front of a piece of art is like putting a plastic wrap on furniture."

COMMENTS

I have laminated most of my photos that are used in healthcare facilities. The lamination is resistant to disinfectants, doesn't break, doesn't dull the colors, doesn't have any glare, doesn't distort the image, isn't heavy, and is not too expensive.

Posted by: Elaine Poggi | May 10, 2007 at 11:00 AM

SECURITY MOUNTS

Mounting pictures in busy places like hospitals and clinics requires special care. It is important to make theft more difficult and to keep art level in the event it gets bumped.

I asked Puneet Bhasin, vice president at Artline, a contract framer, for some suggestions.

> Although the initial idea behind security hardware for artwork was created because artwork was disappearing from walls, security hardware is now also used to make sure that artwork stays level.

> We have gotten a lot of requests for security hardware because it also keeps artwork from falling down. The traditional way of hanging art was to use hanging wire on the back of the frame. Later, people drilled holes into frames to secure the artwork. This posed a couple of issues: It created a look that said you don't trust people, and the drilling caused the frame to crack, which created splinters.

> Security hardware is mounted on the back of the picture. There are typically three brackets installed. One on each of the top corners and third in middle of the bottom frame. A 'T' screw secures the artwork, which requires a special wrench (or key) to turn the T screw. You only need one T screw per picture, (which is installed on the bottom bracket).

> Typically security hardware ranges from $1.50 to $10 per picture. Some companies, like Artline, don't even charge for security hardware. A lot of times, a hospital will contact us because they had artwork locally framed, and the gallery or frame shop doesn't even know what security hardware is.

For instructions on security hardware, go to www.artlinewholesalers.com.

CAN FRAMING BE GREEN?

The trend in architecture and design is toward using "green" or environmentally friendly methods and materials. More and more projects are LEED certified. I wondered about how this might be applied to art that is matted and framed for healthcare. I asked Puneet Bhasin, vice president at Artline, a contract framer, for some suggestions.

Ask your framer to make sure that most of the papers used in the mat boards are produced out of recycled fiber. In addition, only environmentally friendly colorants should be used.

Whenever it's not feasible to use recycled fiber, make sure the source material is from responsible mills that use tree farms for their wood pulp. Therefore, a tree is planted for every tree consumed.

Make sure that the frame shop recycles all the paper products they use. Check to see if the wood moldings are cut from continually recycled forests, whose trees are planted, nurtured, and harvested on a rotation basis.

GALLERY WRAP – PROS AND CONS

In the last few years, my canvas prints have become much more popular. It is easy to see why. Canvas prints have a lot of advantages over paper prints:

- Canvas is much less expensive to frame than paper
- Canvas prints have no glare because they aren't covered with glass

Properly framing canvas is a matter of taste. Many frame shops promote "gallery wrap," where the canvas wraps around the sides. That is not my personal preference. My background is in oil painting. Oil paintings would never be wrapped around the sides. In museums, one would never see an image on canvas wrapped on the sides of the stretcher bars.

My preference is to have the white canvas show on the sides and leave the picture unframed. That is a very contemporary look.

Alternatively, a thin wooden strip can be applied on all sides, which makes the print appear more finished.

Why do frame shops promote gallery wrap? I think it's because it is much easier and faster to stretch the canvas if one does not have to precisely align the image to the front. With white edges, it is tricky to get the front of the image to align exactly.

COMMENTS

Henry...I love the canvas image from the NW. It looks great in my conference room. I have several other canvases of yours. I have used all approaches to framing and edge detail. This time, since I was placing this piece in an area without windows, I chose a thin wood frame with space to float canvas to make it almost appear as a window. The wood frame makes it look a little more finished also.

Posted by: Beth Worthington | November 03, 2008 at 10:11 AM

PROTECTING ART IN HOSPITALS

Canvas prints can be very effective in hospital settings. Canvas has several advantages:

- No glass
- No glare
- Lower framing costs
- Size—they can be big

However, I am frequently asked: "How do canvas prints hold up in a busy hospital?" "What happens when the cleaning staff wipes them with a wet cloth?" "How will canvas prints tolerate children with peanut butter and jelly on their fingers?"

If the canvas print has a protective coating applied, it should do just fine. Over the last several years, I have sold hundreds of canvas prints, and there has never been a problem. But I'm always looking for ways to improve.

One problem with the protective coating I had been using was that it had to be applied after the canvas was stretched or it would crack. That meant passing that job to the frame shops. Now I have discovered a coating that can be applied by me before the prints are stretched.

I've tested this varnish and it is amazingly tough—almost bulletproof. I've scrubbed them with soapy rags and tried to scratch them with a kitchen fork. The prints came through just fine. However, I had to build a sealed spray room with a strong exhaust fan and good lights.

COMMENTS

Great spray room! It seems like a good idea for you to have control of varnishing your own photos.

Thanks again for the wonderful tour of your property last week. Even though I picked up a few ticks, I really enjoyed seeing how you work and learning from you!

Posted by: Elaine Poggi | May 22, 2008 at 12:24 AM

Elaine, it was great to have you here last week! Sorry about the ticks, one of the occupational hazards for nature photographers in Missouri.

Posted by: Henry Domke | May 22, 2008 at 08:07 AM

So don't keep us in the dark! What kind of spray are you using?

Posted by: Joanie San Chirico | May 23, 2008 at 06:26 PM

The spray I am using is called Glamour II. It is made by Breathing Color. I experimented with others, but this one looked the best and at the same time offered great protection. I blend it 70 percent matte/30 percent glossy.

The canvas I have decided to use is called "Epson Premium Canvas Matte." I tried others, but this one has a luscious surface that holds more detail than others because it has less "tooth."

Incidentally, I am buying all my varnish, paper, canvas, ink, and printers from a company called InkjetArt.com. They are VERY good to deal with.

Posted by: Henry Domke | May 24, 2008 at 09:18 AM

Thanks Henry! I've been using Eco-Print Shield with okay results, but I'm glad to see that there's something else I can try. I've heard other good things about Glamour II.

Posted by: Joanie San Chirico | May 24, 2008 at 01:20 PM

I too feel that canvas is the way to go for healthcare. However, those that follow the Planetree seem to want everything under glass. Also, the issue of healthcare carts that damage the canvases through their day-to-day use . . . those sharp corners can do some damage. Mounting the canvases on a sturdy back still does not stop that real menace from doing damage. However, points can be made for works behind glass . . . Plexi is usually substituted in these more detrimental areas. I have been exploring possibilities of other surfaces that might be more advantageous for healthcare prints. The search continues. Thanks for your magic and help, Doc Henry.

Posted by: a.musia | November 17, 2008 at 12:12 PM

COMMON FRAMING MISTAKES

Tim Carroll has years of experience framing art. He meticulously framed many of my prints over the last decade. I asked him to reflect on the most common framing mistakes.

- Bringing your spouse (or significant other) with you to select framing for 'your' artwork. I often considered getting a marriage counselor's license since I did more of that than recommending double mats. Too many cooks can definitely spoil the frame job.
- Skimping on the frame or other materials to save a couple of dollars. Often the difference between a 'Wow!' framing job and a 'Good' framing job is only $25. The most expensive frame is not by any means always the best, though. The point is to try and find what you really like first, and then worry about the budget. A year later, you won't think about the cost, but you will regret not having done it right the first time.
- Making everything match. Unexpected color combinations will add excitement to your piece. When someone shows up with a plaid couch pillow or their prized Shih Tzu and wants to match the matting, then you may be in trouble. No question, you have to take into account the décor of the area that the piece will be in, but keep the focus on the artwork.

Carroll and his wife recently sold their business, Cottonstone Gallery, in Jefferson City, Mo.

MURALS AND BACKLIT PANELS

HOW BIG CAN A PICTURE BE ENLARGED?

I often get asked to make pictures big, sometimes VERY big.

For example, this week I'm having a print of a single coneflower installed in Georgia. It's more than 26 feet wide. Some pictures enlarge better than others. There are a lot of issues behind this, mostly technical stuff like megapixels and very careful attention to technique.

Part of the issue is the subject matter. Some things just look better big. Landscapes with a lot of fine detail (leaves and blades of grass) are harder to enlarge than close-ups of flowers. There are primarily two things that go wrong with images that are enlarged too much:

- They can show pixelation where the edges of things can start to show "jaggies"
- They can appear out of focus

Viewing distance is another variable that is critical. If you are going to be 5 feet or more from the print, then you won't be able to see the flaws. But if you look at a huge print (a billboard, for example), from 5 inches away, it will look like nonsense.

So how big can a picture be enlarged? It depends on each image and the viewing distance. You have to take it on a case-by-case basis.

WHEN TO USE PANORAMAS

This morning I have been working with two interior designers (Amy Pressman and Judy Girod) to come up with images to fill entire walls. Each of these separate healthcare projects has walls that are much wider than they are tall—about 30'x 6'.

Most photographic images fit an aspect ratio of 3:2. If you crop a single image down to 5:1, you don't have much of the original image left, and what's left suffers from excessive enlargement.

The solution is to use images that were created to fit a wide aspect ratio: panoramas. With the transition from film to digital cameras, this has become much easier. Photographers can now set up their cameras on a tripod to take a series of images from left to right. Those images can then be "stitched" together digitally in the computer, and you end up with a panorama.

Many of my panoramas were created from six individual images. So I have gone from 16.7 megapixels (which, after cropping, would only be about 4 megapixels), to an 85-megapixel image. Because there is about 20 times as much data to work with, it tolerates a lot more enlargement.

Amy Pressman is an interior designer and owner of Pressman Design Studio in East Greenbush, New York, and Judy Girod is director of interior design at Lothrop Associates Architects in Valhalla, New York. Pressman and Girod both have extensive experience in selecting art for healthcare facilities.

COMMENTS

Wow! I love what you have done with a sterile and colorless space. The pictures of nature create calm and happiness in healthcare places that would otherwise create stress and nervousness. Good work!
Posted by: Annemarie Johnson | October 16, 2007 at 08:18 AM

IS BIGGER BETTER?

Today I was listening to a podcast where Brooks Jensen scoffed at the idea of bigger prints. His discussion was triggered by some recent product announcements for cameras with more megapixels and printers that will print 64 inches wide. He laughed and said, "How big is big enough?" then made a joke about how Americans always want things bigger.

While it may be true that in general, Americans prefer things bigger just on principle (from hamburgers to houses), I think he has not looked carefully at the healthcare market.

For healthcare and commercial spaces, bigger art is better. A 2' x 3' print looks very small if it is in a large room. An 8" x 10" print disappears and would almost never fit. I don't even sell prints that small. Recently, I've been sending out prints up to 14 feet long and mocked up a mural 158 feet long. (Sadly, it did not get printed.)

Historically, photographers have thought of an 8" x 10" print as a standard big print. That size was dictated by what their enlarger could do. We are now in an era where digital inkjet printing allows prints that are larger and higher in quality than we could have dreamed of a decade ago. In the world of print publishing (where Jensen lives) and in the world of the Internet, big does not matter; but for the rest of us, it does.

COMMENTS

Yes, Henry, bigger is better in a healthcare facility. While my mother was in the hospital, she was not able to get around very well and spent most of her time in her bed. The hospital had placed an abstract work of art on the wall in front of her bed. It was approximately 10 inches by 15 inches. Since she wasn't wearing her glasses most of the time, she couldn't figure out what was on the art work. She couldn't see it. Thus, from my experience, I think the ideal size for a work of art in a hospital room is about 20 inches by 30 inches. It is big enough to see from the bed, yet small enough to fit in tight spaces.
Posted by: Elaine Poggi | September 11, 2007 at 12:35 PM

Well said. I suppose there is always a reason and a circumstance for

almost everything. I agree, my small prints would look puny in your hospital display, but a hospital-display sized print would be overwhelming in my lap in the La-Z-Boy. I do love photography's versatility! Brooks Jensen, Editor, LensWork Publishing
Posted by: Brooks Jensen | September 11, 2007 at 04:31 PM

BACKLIT PANELS (PART 1)

As I examined a patient last week, she said, "Why don't you have art on the ceiling so that when I'm on the exam table, I have something to look at other than ceiling tiles?" Good question!

Then yesterday afternoon, I got this email from a contractor in New York: "One our clients . . . is budgeting a renovation of a large indoor atrium that has a solid ceiling center surrounded by skylights." He wanted to know if I could provide him with the art.

Ever since I saw "A Sudden Gust of Wind (after Hokusai) 1993" by the artist Jeff Wall, I've been interested in backlit panels. This post is simply a brief introduction. I will explore this topic in more detail in later posts.

One thing I learned is that the backlit panels of translucent plastic are called "light lenses." Standard sizes are either 2' x 2' or 2' x 4'. They can be grouped in a grid like a mosaic to create large images and are very easy to install. They are most often used on ceilings, but can also be used in walls.

The fact that the light is transmitted through the light lens creates an effect that is closer to stained glass than looking at conventional art where light is reflected.

My initial research turned up three businesses that focus on the healthcare industry:

- Art Research Institute, Ltd. (www.visualtherapy.com)
- Ceiling Scenes (www.ceilingscenes.com)
- TESS USA, Inc. (www.tessusainc.com)

BACKLIT PANELS (PART 2)

A FedEx truck delivered a sturdy wooden box on Friday. After I unscrewed a side panel, I found a very thin lightbox with one of my images installed.

Today I called Tom Kitchell at International Linear Matrix in Florida to ask him a few questions about the lightbox he sent me.

How is your lightbox different from others on the market?

Ours is one of the thinnest lightboxes available—it is less than 2 inches thick, even when it is double-sided. Also, ours is unique in that it is made and serviced in the United States.

What would a lightbox like the one you sent me cost if a hospital were to buy one?

A 2' x 3' lightbox retails for $480.

How long do the tubes last before they have to be changed?

The fluorescent bulbs are rated for 20,000 hours. That is 2.5 years of continuous use. We use T4 fluorescent bulbs, which are standard —very easy to find and easy to replace.

Do you typically supply the printed image to go in the lightbox, or do your customers tend to do that locally?

We can go either way. The images we print are done on a Kodak N-CAD printer using Kodak Premium Backlit film that is 7 mm thick.

Is there anything else you would like to say?

Because our boxes are made at our factory in Florida, we can give very quick turn-around times, typically seven to 10 days. All of our orders are custom. We can make a lightbox of any size up to 4' x 10'.

For more information, go to www.ilmusa.com.

BACKLIT PANELS (PART 3)

I'm continuing to gather more information on backlit panels. Recently, I've been corresponding with Cindy Tlachac of Everbrite Lighting Technologies.

I asked her to explain how Everbrite Lighting Technologies is different from the competition.

We are the lighting designer and manufacturer; we even manufacture our own circuit boards. We produce a superior product; our system uses 1-watt LEDs, which must be driven at constant current, or in other words regulated current. By doing this, we can assure the LEDs will last their expected lifetime. Others use resistors in between the LEDs to regulate the current. This is not the way 1-watt LEDs should be driven, and by doing this, they are increasing the odds of premature failure.

Our lighting installs easily and requires no additional parts; simply plug and play.

We have been in business since 1927, and offer a three-year warranty on all MedLux products. Others do not design or manufacturer anything—they purchase from someone else. Who will the customer go back to if they lose their resource for lighting?

Another major difference is that we also offer large-format lightboxes. We offer 2' x 2', 2' x 4', 3' x 3', 3' x 4', and 4' x 4', which provide the customer with an image that has fewer divisions. Since customers are spending a lot of money on a beautiful image, they would prefer to have the least amount of interruptions in the image as possible.

For more information, visit www.e-l-t.com.

SKYLINE DESIGN TOUR

Yesterday I took an extended tour of the factory and offices at Skyline Design in Chicago. I was impressed!

Most of you probably know Skyline already, but if you don't, they are the preeminent manufacturer of architectural glass in North America. They specialize in custom-carved, painted, and etched architectural glass.

Inside the rather modest red brick exterior, the factory space extends over thousands of square feet. I kept thinking we had seen it all, and then we came to yet another basketball-court sized room. Despite the fact that they were very busy with orders, the production floors were clean, well-lit, and the air quality was good.

Designers and architects I have worked with around the United States always tell me the same thing about Skyline Design: "They are wonderful to work with," and, "They have the nicest people, and they also make the best glass, by far!"

My impressions echo that. Of the hundred people that work there, they all seemed to be happy. One reason they may be so happy is that there seems to be a culture of creative playfulness that starts with the owner, Charlie Rizzo; he has a twinkle in his eye.

The staff was obviously very passionate about their work. The designers I met approach their job as artists. The sales and management staff share the same creative vision. It was very exciting to sense the energy that was there; creative, yet also professional.

If you are ever in Chicago, I encourage you to arrange a tour. For more information, go to www.skydesign.com.

TRENDS

DIGITAL PHOTO FRAME—THE FUTURE OF HOSPITAL ART?

Prediction: Within 10 years, flat panel television screens will replace prints as wall art in patient rooms.

Sales of flat panel displays have been remarkable. Since they are used in all computer displays and most television screens, there has been a tremendous drive to reduce price and increase quality. Even Bill Gates uses flat panel monitors to display fine art in his mansion.

The displays are starting to get into a price range where they could be considered for wall art in patient rooms. Last week I found one on Amazon.com for $180, and I thought I would try it out. It arrived today and I've been setting it up to see how it compares to prints on a wall.

My initial impression: Close, but not ready for prime time.

Having the image illuminated from behind is very pleasing and eliminates the need to consider proper lighting.

Image quality is poor compared to my prints, but I think that it will satisfy most patients. High-def monitors that look better are available, but they cost more.

Having slideshows with hundreds of images is easy to set up and may be more appealing to some viewers than a static image.

Patients could easily add their own pictures to personalize their rooms. I can see people having pictures of their grandchildren or their pets on screen.

The screen is only 6" x 8," much too small for wall art in a patient room. Bigger monitors cost much more.

The material quality is not good enough to survive in a busy hospital setting. This is really something for your grandmother's desk.

Setting up the Aluratek 10.5 digital photo frame was not easy, and I am used to working with technical gear. It took four phone calls to tech support to get everything running right. I'm happy to say that the tech support people were nice and knowledgeable.

Lots of little annoying things that are specific to this display and not this general idea.

It does not work with Macintosh computers, only PCs (and I use a Mac). It does not work with "progressive" JPGs, only standard JPGs (and of course, I always save my JPGs as progressive).

The optimal image size for the JPGs is 1,024 x 768 pixels, but that information wasn't printed anywhere in the brief manual or on the box.

DOES ART SPREAD SUPERBUGS?

Superbugs in hospitals have everyone scared, and for good reason. Doctors and researchers fear that these bacteria may become entrenched in hospitals, threatening the very patients who go there for treatment.

Understanding superbugs is important for designers. Jain Malkin, in her new book, wrote: "Infection control is such a big issue today; it has to be the number one thing that architects and designers understand."

To see if the art in hospitals might cause infections, I contacted an expert, Mark Winton, M.D. Dr. Winton is a board-certified specialist in infectious disease. When I worked as a family practice doctor, I always referred to him the cases that stumped me. The following is based on an email interview we had this week.

Can art prints contribute in any meaningful way to the spread of hospital-acquired infections?

Not that I am aware of. They are no more potential fomites than the walls.

Should hospitals attempt to disinfect art prints? If so, how?

No disinfection is needed. The chance of art prints retaining resistant organisms is very small. The pigments in paint (and inks) tend to be antibacterial in nature.

What are the major contributors to all hospital-acquired infections, especially with superbugs?

- Instrumentation (putting devices in patients)
- Poor hand washing
- Overuse of antibiotics

The current issue of The New Yorker has an article called "Superbugs: The New Generation of Resistant Infections is Almost Impossible to Treat."

COMMENTS

I agree with the sentiment of Jain Malkin's comment that infection control is one of the most important things that architects and designers understand. In regard to Dr. Winton's comments—I sincerely hope we are not seeing a lot of carpet on the walls!

Seriously though, C. difficile and MRSA are indiscriminate when it comes to taking up residence on a surface and can live on those surfaces for weeks. I have collected data that showed bacteria residing on smooth flooring that was not found on adjacent carpeting in a patient corridor/nursing station area. Any floor or table or object in a patient room may harbor pathogens if not adequately cleaned and disinfected.

You have to remember that technology continues to press forward in spite of ourselves. Synthetic carpets (rolled goods and tiles) with non-permeable backings are successfully used in hospitals all across the country. Some hospitals prefer to use smooth surface flooring because they believe that it is more cleanable and is perceived to be cleaner by those occupying the building.

However, there are other issues in regard to the indoor environment and attributes of various flooring materials to consider when specifying hospital flooring. Molds, like aspergillus, will grow on anything when the indoor environmental conditions are right and there is a food source. Again, proper maintenance is key to a healthy indoor patient environment.

Posted by: Debra Harris, Ph.D. | August 13, 2008 at 09:26 AM

TRENDS—BIG, BOLD, AND COLORFUL

Many of my images are used by designers in very large formats. I asked designer Tara Hill to share her thoughts on trends in healthcare art:

> We are seeing 'images' used on grand scales to convey thought or feeling. These images are being used to provide an 'experience' to the patient and families. Much like a grand Georgia O'Keefe vs. a small wall print. Art is becoming graphic in feel. I think this is because graphic tends to be more dynamic, i.e., it provides a stronger experience. (But not all of our clients like the graphic look, but it certainly is a trend.) Last is color. More bold, dynamic, saturated tones, or clear color and contrasting values in graphic depictions (like your big close up of flowers), are being used to enliven a space, make it less institutional . . . once again, providing a dimensional experience.

Tara R. Hill, ASID, is a registered interior designer and founder of LittleFISH Think Tank.

TRENDS—BIG NATURE PHOTOS

JoAnna Rogers and I got to know each other as we worked together on the art program for Ohio Health's brand new Dublin Methodist Hospital outside of Columbus.

I asked her to share some ideas on current trends in healthcare art:

There is more and more interest in the display of artwork that represents nature. Not only in the medium of paintings, but photography is becoming more and more popular.

Artwork and photography of landscapes are particularly effective displayed in patient areas, such as patient rooms, exam rooms, and treatment areas. A beautiful landscape can transform one to a beautiful setting and distract from the patient's condition, which may be stressful.

Another growing trend is the use of modern abstract art. Bold colors and textures. Art as an extension to the design of the hospitals many times would translate as works that are more about color and texture, rather than a subject.

Large-scale works, creative compositions of multiple pieces. Displayed in public areas, such as atrium lobbies, waiting areas, staff lounges, dining areas, etc., are displayed similarly to hospitality or corporate environments.

Designers are interested in the integration of artwork into the overall design concept. It is the finishing touch of the built design. A seamless connection between the selection of artwork and the interior architecture is an important key of integrated design.

Rogers is an interior designer at NBBJ in New York City.

CONSENSUS: NATURE IMAGES ARE BEST!

Jean Young, president of Young + Co., Inc. in San Diego and a board member for the Coalition for Health Environments Research, was clear and concise in her description about what trends she sees for art in healthcare:

The concepts are nature, and not abstracts.

There is a thought about the larger overall imagery for waiting rooms then drilling down into more detail-type imagery in the back areas. It needs to be art that is understood and recognizable.

In thinking about what Young and other experts have said, there is a clear consensus on what is best for healthcare: non-threatening realistic nature art. I keep hearing the same answer from designers, art consultants, and scientific researchers.

If evidence-based design says that today, does that mean that the answer will be the same in 20 years or in 200 years? For "hard" scientific information once a truth is found, it should be true regardless of the era. Mix two parts of hydrogen and one part oxygen, and you get water.

When I think about the right answers in design and in art, I think that part of the answer is due to trends, to fashion. Hence, what was right in the 50s does not fit today.

I've been surprised that so few people have questioned the negative statements about abstract art in healthcare. Being a contrarian by nature, I'm suspicious when everyone agrees on something. Does anyone disagree with this?

COMMENTS

Henry, I can tell you what the trend was back in the 1300s and 1400s. The artists painted doctors with halos!!! The idea was to convince the patients that the doctors were like saints and that they should have confidence in their knowledge . . . Art in Italian hospitals back then was religious often with angels hanging around the patient. And some of the art is still there!

Posted by: Elaine Poggi | May 03, 2007 at 05:19 AM

Hi Henry! I can't argue with the designers and the art consultants, because I don't have any data to back up my opinion. It's only an opinion, or a gut feeling, and not a fact.

The emphasis on realistic nature-centered art makes me think of catering to the lowest common denominator. It's like saying that people are too stupid or too ignorant to be able to handle abstract art, or else they're too threatened by it. Come on! How scary can an abstract painting be?

I'm also puzzled because I have seen abstract art in healthcare facilities, and some of my abstract art is in healthcare facilities.

It seems to me that every doctor's office I go to is decorated with ethereal sorts of soft abstracts that don't have any specific content or meaning. So when did this nature-centered theme thing spring up?
Posted by: Cassie | May 03, 2007 at 11:38 AM

Cassie: I find your comments about "catering to the lowest common denominator" interesting. But I ask: is it bad to give people what they want?

However, I disagree that it suggests people are "too stupid or too ignorant to be able to handle abstract art." It might help you to read chapter 7 of "Putting Patients First," and you might want to refer back to my posts in the controversial category.
Posted by: hdomke | May 04, 2007 at 07:16 AM

Jean Young stresses that art be recognizable and "understood." While the type of work you currently practice certainly doesn't befuddle the viewer, neither is nature explicit of meaning, nor easily understood. Which might explain part of its attraction. The other part would be that plants and animals act as familiar symbols, prompting memories and emotions from every viewer. As well known to us as our memories are, in equal share the subjects, which prompted them, are figurative and curiosity worthy. What a combination!
Posted by: Bill | May 04, 2007 at 09:09 AM

Henry: Now you're venturing into the area of "What is art?" Should art be dictated by the audience, or is it about personal expression or communication?

Strangely enough, I'm currently working on a series of abstracts dictated by my licensing agent. When it comes to corporations and hotels, abstracts sell.
Posted by: Cassie | May 04, 2007 at 11:45 AM

Bill: It is interesting that you bring up memories. One comment I hear frequently when people look at my landscapes is that they remember being in that space—"Did you take that on my grand-parents' farm?"

This phenomenon has also been demonstrated repeatedly in studies that have been done by others. Landscape images tend to evoke positive memories. That helps provide a pleasant escape from a frightening experience (like being in a medical building).
Posted by: hdomke | May 04, 2007 at 01:24 PM

Cassie: You asked the great question: "Should art be dictated by the audience, or is it about personal expression or communication?" One thing that "evidence-based design" would argue is that the key consideration is the patient and the healing process. The idea of self-expression in this setting has no meaning.

One has to only ask how art functions. How does it affect the patient? Second, what impact does it have on their family and the staff?

This is quite different than the art that I learned about in art school. It takes a little getting used to, but the more I think about it the more it makes sense.
Posted by: hdomke | May 04, 2007 at 01:57 PM

I think pictures of nature and natural beauty are calming and soothing. I do not understand abstract art. I am not an artist and have not studied art. I do notice pictures in buildings. Henry's pictures of flowers with drops of dew display the beauty of nature that I don't take the time to enjoy and appreciate, even though I know it's there. He captures other detail of butterflies, birds, and plants which makes them quite fascinating. They can be a topic of conversation for anyone.
Posted by: Joyce | May 04, 2007 at 09:46 PM

Florence Nightingale writing in her 1859 Notes on Nursing: "The effect in sickness of beautiful objects, of variety of objects is hardly at all appreciated . . . brilliancy of colour in the objects . . . are actual means of recovery."
Posted by: Lillian Fitzgerald | May 05, 2007 at 09:06 AM

POLICY FOR ART DONATIONS

What if a wealthy patron decides to donate their valuable Roy Lichtenstein paintings to your hospital?

Hospitals are wise to have a gift-acceptance policy regarding art donations. Patrons of the hospital may have art that they want to donate, but if the terms are not spelled out clearly, it can backfire. At HCD08, Kathy Hathorn, CEO and creative director of American Art Resources, had a few words of advice on what to include in the document:

- Donors relinquish all rights to donated work once the donation has been made.
- There is no promise to display the donated art.
- Donated art that is displayed could be subject to future removal or relocation.
- In circumstances where a donated work of art has great monetary value, the hospital may choose to sell the work and use the funds to support the healing mission.
- Encourage prospective donors to visit the facility to see examples of the type of art that you would like to receive.
- All donated art and frames must be in excellent condition and ready to display.

COMMON MISCONCEPTIONS ABOUT "LOCAL" ART

Using local art for hospitals is a growing trend for many good reasons. It is nice to support local artists, and they might have art that reflects unique features of the community. However, at HCD08, Kathy Hathorn, CEO and creative director of American Art Resources, warned about the downside of insisting on local art.

Common misconceptions about "local" art include that it is:

- Within the budget
- High quality
- Appropriate for patients
- Appropriate for the project

Just because local art is made nearby does not mean it will be a better value. It pays to shop around.

Local art may be interesting, but it might not be appropriate for patients. A cactus picture, for example, may be considered a "nature photo," but that does not mean it is appropriate for display in hospitals. All those sharp needles can remind patients of blood draws and injections.

To help keep these problems under control, Hathorn suggests having written goals for the art program. Have a clear definition about what "local" means. She suggests giving priority to quality over locality. To make sure you reach the largest pool of artists, put out a formal "call for artists."

COMMENTS

I think if the art is not from the region where it will be placed, then caption plaques might be a good idea. By far, "Where is that picture taken?" is THE most common question we are asked when presenting at shows and exhibits. People seem to crave relevance to a photograph. I agree that there is too much emphasis on the subject matter of the art being from the region of the installation. As long as people know where it is, it seems to resolve the issue. As my friend and wonderful painter Mike Savage says, "Art is simple—either you like it or you don't!"
Posted by: Kevin Sink | February 03, 2009 at 09:43 AM

The University of Michigan Health Care System hospital in Ann Arbor has a gift of art program that includes exhibitions of art by local artists (I was one) throughout sections of the hospital. Here's the website: http://www.med.umich.edu/goa/programs.htm. For the hospital, it's a low budget way to have art on display. For artists, a great way to gain exposure. A small commission on sales goes to help support the program.
Posted by: Patrice Erickson | February 04, 2009 at 12:52 PM

DIFFERENT ART FOR DIFFERENT AREAS

When I asked my sister Beth, an interior designer in St. Louis, what she wanted to see discussed on this blog, she said, "What art should be used in different locations of the hospital?"

After doing a Google search, I came up with an excellent article by Kathy Hathorn, president of American Art Resources in Houston, a consulting firm that works exclusively with the healthcare industry. It is titled, "The Use of Art in Healthcare." Hathorn is one of the most experienced art consultants in healthcare. She has written and lectured extensively on the topic. I strongly suggest reading her article for the details.

PROJECT ART—UNIVERSITY OF IOWA HOSPITAL AND CLINICS

One of the leading hospital art programs in the world is located in Iowa City, Iowa. Since it started in 1976, Project Art has grown to include more than 3,600 original works of art and 2,200 reproductions. In addition to their permanent collection, they feature temporary exhibits, an art cart, and performing arts. They even provide art supplies to let patients create art.

They have a comprehensive website that explains all this: www.uihealthcare.com/depts/projectart/.

Since 2002, Adrienne Drapkin has been director of Project Art.

I should mention that besides Project Art, Iowa City is a worthwhile travel destination. It is a charming college town with a population of 62,000. The university has an excellent art museum.

SINGLE-PATIENT HOSPITALS—THE FUTURE?

The hottest trend in today's hospitals is single-patient rooms. This is a vast improvement over the large wards from a hundred years ago. They might have dozens of patients in one room.

But try to imagine a century into the future; dream a little . . . Why not single-patient hospitals?

When you get sick, your physician dispatches a mobile hospital to your driveway. Physicians continue to manage your care via data monitoring and video feeds. Nurse technologists come by once or twice a day to make sure that all the gadgets are properly working and to enjoy a cup of coffee with your family.

Since the trends into nanotechnology, robotics, and biotechnology have matured, you now have everything you need inside your tiny personal hospital. Need surgery? No problem. Miniature robots can do this as you stay in your bed. Lab tests needed? Medication? No problem. This fits into a small suitcase up front.

Your family could sleep in their own beds and come out to visit as they wish. Real home cooked food. Your dog can sleep by your side. Wayfinding worries are a thing of the past; you can't get lost because you are already home.

COMMENTS

Interesting idea, Henry. I'm envisioning the mobile hospital of the future to be more like a DeLorean, though, rather than an Airstream . . .
Posted by: Sara Marberry | September 04, 2007 at 10:29 AM

Sara, of course there will be other options, such as DeLorean Personal Hospitals (as well as Ferrari and Bugatti). But these will carry slightly higher insurance premiums.
Posted by: Henry Domke | September 04, 2007 at 03:08 PM

Put a surfboard on top and an espresso machine inside and I'm there!
Posted by: sknight | September 04, 2007 at 06:17 PM

Wonderful idea. Extremely innovative. It's things like these we are lacking these days. We need more ideas and the ability to make them happen.
Posted by: Anonymous | April 14, 2008 at 03:44 PM

Hi Henry, this is the answer to a long-awaited problem. The mobile unit, one-bed patient unit is an idea for the remote rural areas at this time. And could be prospective into the future in the event of a world-wide disaster or pandemic. The concept is a valid reality, although the cost factors are similar to a portable MRI mobile unit that has started on the East Coast some years ago. Try it, get investors, and watch it grow. Although the costs for maintenance, delivery of the unit (like a regular pickup truck or ? depends on the weight). Would the insurance companies pay the same or more fees for such a mobile unit? The concerns are a critical care patient would need 24/7 until stable. Would the cost warrant the patient fees collected from the insurance company relative to the cost of services for a mobile unit? Anyway, consider all the economic costs for patient costs, the reduced costs to the patient the insurance company. I can go on and on, but wanted to get this topic open for discussion. We are headed toward a big ecological change and to reduce costs to the consumer and to get quality healthcare, may be the best option in say 10–15 years or even less . . . it just depends on what the U.S. government is willing to support, the AMA, the nurses, the patients, the insurance companies, and the state can be difficult too. Airstreams are the toughest—build mobile units today. Thank you, Jackie

Posted by: Ifft-Matisek RN | August 12, 2008 at 03:12 PM

THE FUTURE OF DESIGN: VIRTUAL REALITY

I kept hearing about the on-line virtual reality program called Second Life, but ignored it. It sounded like yet another on-line game for teenage boys. But then my sister Beth kept telling me about how much she enjoyed the program, and that she was designing living spaces to share with others. Then Natalie Zensius, marketing communications manager for The Center for Health Design, wrote an article for the center's blog on the top 10 medical sites on Second Life. She followed up with one on a virtual hospital in England.

Clearly, I misunderstood what this was all about. It was not an action game; it was not a game at all. It is a virtual reality that millions of people around the globe participate in. To find out more, I have registered (for free) with Second Life and have started to learn the basics. To learn more, I asked Zensius to offer her perspective:

Why should interior designers or architects who work in healthcare be interested in Second Life?
Because of the boundless possibilities. This technology only gets better the more people use it. Shared virtual experiences leave participants with a richer, more persistent memory of a sense of place and the information presented there. Architects and designers could create a virtual facility to demonstrate the principles of evidence-based design, both in general terms (highlight principles such as window placement, lighting, color, ambient sound), and in specific terms (show demonstrations of actual research results and designs).

Second Life can be used to demonstrate principles of sustainable architecture, for instance. Even though it doesn't really rain in Second Life, and the Second Life sun doesn't really heat things up, the principles are better demonstrated in an immersive environment. These demonstrations could be an integral part of education and training as well as part of the proposal process.

A Second Life facility could also be used for experiments or research design, either individually or as part of a collaborative work environment. Although many of the ultimate experiments that rely on true patient outcomes could not actually be conducted within Second Life, it would be part of the research design process during brainstorming, concept-formation, and refinement. In addition to design of the physical spaces involved in the research, functional modeling and operational rehearsals for the research can be conducted in Second Life.

Can you imagine that Second Life might be a good way to present the art program for a new hospital? Do you think it will take the place of conventional elevations or conventional 3D renderings?
Using information-sharing, media and virtual demonstrations related to the agenda and goals of a project, and with the addition of true

voice, a 3D virtual space becomes a compelling environment for the client to conceptualize what the finished project will look like. Of course, this would add a whole layer of expense and needed resources to the project, so I think that at this time, it won't replace traditional elevations and renderings because they are more cost effective.

COMMENTS

I have looked at it, but I have a little concern it is too cult-like. People get involved in it and spend lots of time in it. Some people even purchase things through it.

I read your post and understand what you are going for, but it just doesn't seem like a good use of valuable time. Plus, from what I have read, and by virtue of the virtual reality aspect, nothing in it is what it seems. Nothing is really true.

For some people unhappy with their first life, I guess it may provide some escape but I just don't see it. My two cents...
Posted by: George Kopp | October 17, 2007 at 04:29 AM

Some of the biggest brands—Nike, Apple, Coca-Cola—have discovered the untapped potential of Second Life as a means of reaching their markets.

It may seem strange and unfamiliar, but so did the Internet at one point. I say embrace it!
Posted by: Cara | October 29, 2007 at 10:48 AM

TRANSPORTED TO A FARAWAY PLACE

Roger Yee, editor of Healthcare Spaces, gets to see some of the most exciting new hospitals being built in America. I asked him if there was any art installation that caught his eye recently.

If you'd like an interesting example of how art is being used in new healthcare facilities, I would draw your attention to a modest but effective installation, the linear accelerator room at Somerset Medical Center's Steeplechase Cancer Center, Somerville, New Jersey, designed by Array Healthcare Facilities Solutions.

In this windowless space, the design team placed three floor-to-ceiling-high 'picture windows' depicting a forest scene in back-lighted photography. Though designers usually make no attempt to simulate a window with art in this kind of situation, the effect is skillfully reinforced here by an informal and non-institutional setting using wood and wood-like cabinetry and flooring as well as good lighting. The illusion of a forest just beyond the walls is thus surprisingly effective.

Neither the patient nor the medical staff actually believe the art is an actual window into a forest scene, to be sure. However, the composite imagery of the room makes us want to believe it. When we fall under the spell of art, our desire to believe—or suspend our disbelief—may be all we need to feel transported to a faraway place.

Yee, a prolific author, graduated from the Yale School of Architecture. He has 23 books currently listed on Amazon, including the soon-to-be-released "Healthcare Spaces Vol. 4."

HOSPITAL ART IN 100 YEARS

Predicting the future is impossible, but it is fun to fantasize.

If research and technology keep growing at an exponential rate, then we will be in for some interesting art. For one thing, we will know much more about what art really is best for patients. If we are at the birth of evidence-based art today, in a century we should actually have a lot of good evidence.

Plus, art itself will evolve. Artists might not like to admit it, but technology has a major impact on what we create. Music really took off after the industrial revolution brought us machines that could make complex musical instruments like pianos. Painting took off after the industrial revolution allowed for canvas to be mass produced and for paint to be put into tubes.

Digital imaging is not quite two decades old, but its impact is already huge. Imagine how that might change in the next century.

Virtual reality would be the most obvious way for art to evolve. If views of nature are good, how much better would being immersed in virtual nature? It is not too far-fetched to imagine that virtual reality would evolve beyond just images and sound, but incorporate our other senses.

Your hospital room would be transformed into a 3D space complete with sound, touch, and smell. You could feel the gentle breezes and smell the wildflowers that are blooming at your feet. You could reach out and touch them. Not only would you see the stream above flowing, but you could hear it and dip your hand into it.

Today we have a glimpse of interactive virtual reality with Second Life. Could such technology evolve so that friends and family could visit in a virtual way that felt real?

Or, perhaps in 100 years we won't need hospital art because we will no longer need hospitals.

I sure hope I am around to see the changes . . .

NATURE PHOTOGRAPHY

BIRDS ARE BAD?

An experienced healthcare art consultant was looking over my work, and she rejected every single bird picture in my portfolio. Clearly conventional wisdom says: No bird pictures in hospitals!

Do we have any research to support that idea? I asked researcher Dr. Upali Nanda.

> . . . not much data to reach a conclusion; however, some amount of anecdotal evidence does seem to support this.

> One prominent example is the installation of a large-scale sculpture called the "bird garden" that was created as a window view for cancer patients and resulted in adverse reactions amongst patients. This was partly due to the slightly abstract nature of the installation, but some patients saw the birds as frightening predators. I believe the complete reference is in Ulrich's chapter in Claire Cooper Marcus' book.

> If you think about birds' beaks and beady eyes in conjunction with the emotional congruence theory, then it is possible these features, even when harmless and aesthetically gorgeous, can come across as predatory to the emotionally vulnerable. Again, I cannot quote any "hardcore" evidence toward this, but we would love to do a study on it!

What would be involved with doing a study? What would the research cost?

Now cost of a study—that varies. A simple survey with around 60–70 patients will probably cost around $5,000. An outcome-based study would be much more.

If you wanted to do a study, you would have to get in touch with one of the local hospitals (for sample population), a researcher (to design the study), field-assistants (to collect the data), and a statistical consultant (to analyze results). The researcher could be qualified to do both the research design, data collection, and the stat analysis, of course, but if you decide to go with different people, this is the kind of team you will need.

Upali Nanda, Ph.D., is vice president and director of research at American Art Resources.

COMMENTS

I recently had images chosen for Cancer Pavilion in Grand Rapids, Mich. The art consultants did select a brightly-colored orange Baltimore oriole perched in a tree for one of the floors where the theme was sky/air. They also chose two butterfly images to go along with the bird—they hang in a grouping in the main lobby hallway. There are gardens on every level, and I think patients really enjoy having those animal elements paired with the garden.

Posted by: Stacy Niedzwiecki | November 05, 2008 at 08:47 AM

WHAT'S WRONG WITH BEAUTIFUL NATURE?

The November issue of Art in America showed up today. Instead of just skimming for visual stimulation, I read the article, "Behind the Wheel with Henry Wessel," by Melissa Feldman.

The article explained how in the 1970s, Wessel was influential in the shift in photography away from the traditional "beatific scenes of untainted nature, in the manner of Ansel Adams and Edward Weston, to casual or clinical pictures of the landscape including its man-made elements. . . ."

In today's world of fine art photography, the path looking at the banal rather than the majestic and the polluted rather than the immaculate is still being followed, at least at the very high-end galleries, which serve connoisseurs. One of my closest friends teaches fine art photography at Texas A&M, and he specializes in photographs of toxic waste dumps.

For years it has puzzled me why "high art" would shift so forcefully against all things beautiful. Is this just a transient shift in taste? Why do I enjoy these images?

If you want to learn more, there is some excellent information about Henry Wessel at the Rena Bransten Gallery website. I have an excellent book on Henry Wessel that accompanied the exhibit earlier this year at the San Francisco Museum of Modern Art.

COMMENTS

Ah, my friend, I'm not turning my back on beauty. I'm trying to expand the idea of what can be beautiful. I think most of us can agree that a flower is beautiful, what's the argument—the thesis—in that? But a toxic waste site? Beautiful?! Really? There's the discussion!
Posted by: vaughn | October 29, 2007 at 10:53 PM

Perhaps in order to appreciate the beautiful, we must be exposed to the ugly...
Posted by: Elaine Poggi | October 31, 2007 at 10:46 AM

I've been reading "Postmodernism" by Glenn Ward, and the author is saying that in this era we are starting to question everything... not just Clement Greenberg's vision of what is the best high art... this is a good thing... upon questioning that about Vaughn's work I think it is beautiful and that is part of the dilemma...a beautiful toxic landscape.
Posted by: Carol Thompson | October 31, 2007 at 11:04 AM

SHOWCASE OF NATURE PHOTOGRAPHY – NANPA

If you are looking to find wildlife and nature images for a healthcare setting, consider looking at the images created by members of the

North American Nature Photography Association. NANPA is the key organization supporting nature photographers in America. I've been a member for several years.

Each year they hold a photo contest to showcase the skills of the members. This year's contest, called NANPA Members' Showcase, has some outstanding work.

One thing you will appreciate is that they make contacting the photographer easy. If you see an image you like, there are links right next to it to email that photographer or to go to the website. The on-line "showcase" features 100 diverse photographs from some of the best nature photographers in the world.

They also have published a high-quality 96-page book that shows the winners. It is a great bargain for only $15. I think it would be a great reference to have on hand if you specify art. For more information, go to www.nanpa.org.

IS ALL WILDLIFE ART MEDIOCRE?

"There's an unfortunate chasm between wildlife art and what's perceived as fine art," says sculptor Bart Walter.

Indeed, I think most art connoisseurs consider realistic wild animal pictures to be "not worthy," more craft than art.

There is a museum dedicated to art like this: The National Museum of Wildlife Art in Jackson Hole, Wyo. According to a story in the Los Angeles Times, the museum wants to improve the public's attitude. The story is called, "Wildlife Art Museum Seeks More Humans."

Apparently not enough people know about this new 51,000-sq-ft museum that houses a collection of 4,000 works of art. The director of the museum, James C. McNutt, is quoted in the article:

> There's tension between first- and second-class art and who says what art is. Representational art is getting back into the mainstream in ways it hasn't been for a while. But there are still quite a few museums that won't hang this kind of work, that don't care about it.

Any thoughts on why wildlife art is held in such contempt? Do people consider it to be too close to kitsch?

Even if wildlife art is considered inappropriate in most of today's museums, what about in hospitals and medical clinics?

COMMENTS

I think the issue is less about how wildlife art may be regarded among critics and more about the affect it has on people . . .

I notice that your website galleries feature "images to help people of all ages connect to the timeless beauty of nature." Art featuring wildlife doesn't necessarily reflect nature's beauty, but I'm glad to see that you include some wildlife in your galleries. James C. McNutt, Ph.D., President & CEO, National Museum of Wildlife Art
Posted by: James C. McNutt, Ph.D. | July 21, 2008 at 04:38 PM

THE HISTORY OF HEALING ART

The idea that views of nature could be healing did not start with Roger Ulrich's research published in Science magazine in 1984. In Western Civilization, that idea can be traced back at least five centuries. This came as a total surprise to me tonight as I was reading a book on the history of landscape painting. Here is a quote:

> Already in Alberti's 'Ten Books on Architecture' from around 1450, we find that in the decoration of private houses, 'rural landscapes, harbors, hunting and fishing, bathing scenes, pastoral plays, flowers, and lush greenery' were sure to elevate one's spirits. Alberti felt that paintings could definitely influence a viewer's state of health. Green was calming, and people suffering from fever might find relief by gazing at painted fountains, rivers, and flowing streams. Alvise Cornaro took up the same argument; nothing was better than villa life and lovely landscape views for physical and mental health.
>
> From page 81 of "Landscape Painting, a History," by Nils Buttner.

RELIGIOUS ART

ART FOR RELIGIOUS HOSPITALS (PART 1)

I asked Kathy Hathorn, president and principal-in-charge of American Art Resources, to share some insight into the special requirements for providing art for religious hospitals.

Is the selection of art for hospitals with religious affiliations different from other hospitals?

There seems to be a trend away from literal representation of denominational icons, such as the crucifix. Instead, faith-based organizations are looking for subtly conveying spirituality, rather than being overt.

Why is this happening?

Two reasons. First, in North America and in Europe, fewer people identify with a specific denomination. In fact, there are fewer people attending church.

Second, there has been an influx of people from around the globe into our country, people from different cultures and traditions. These people are not just located on the coasts, they are all over America. Even in small towns that you think of as being homogeneous.

The churches, which own these hospitals, do not want to offend those who are not of their faith. The idea is to welcome all, to be inclusive. This is a significant change over the last 20 to 30 years and, the truth of the matter, it just makes better business sense.

As an example, for the stained glass in chapels within hospitals, there is a trend away from literal images. Instead, there are more abstracted images that suggest spirituality.

If there is a trend away from the overtly religious, what subjects are taking their place?

There is a movement toward the use of the natural; nature is being brought inside. This can be either purely representational or of abstracted nature, but we don't see pure abstractions being used routinely.

THE WINNER: INCORPORATING FAITH-BASED ARTWORK INTO THE MODERN HEALTHCARE ENVIRONMENT

Eva Payne, an interior designer at TRO Jung|Brannen in Birmingham, won my contest to describe her most challenging healthcare art project and how she solved it. The problem she dealt with was incorporating faith-based artwork into the modern healthcare environment. Here is what she wrote:

Artwork selection may be the most subjective area of an interior designer's work. Although many studies exist that suggest that certain subject matter and color palettes may aid in the creation of the healing environment, selling those concepts to a rural, up-and-coming faith-based hospital administrative staff is another matter.

Artwork selection has been the most contentious ongoing issue with a client wishing to focus primarily on their faith mission. As a community hospital, the budget was not available to commission artwork, and most prints and lithographs currently available with a Christian theme were not particularly sophisticated artistically. Given this lack of quality images, it is quite difficult to assemble an art package large enough to address all of the needs of a hospital. After working through several art consultants and a selective hospital art committee, we were able to compromise in several ways.

A few images of churches and crosses were utilized; bible verses were inscribed in mats under peaceful landscape images. In lieu of artwork in some areas, metal letters were used simply with the words such as, 'Faith,' 'Hope,' and 'Love,' from Corinthians I. Moving in this direction made the committee more comfortable with using some botanical images to evoke a soothing, nature-oriented theme with photographs of flowers and regional landscapes. Although getting to this solution was quite trying at times, the project achieved both the goal of inspiring patients and visitors with the Christian message, while creating a modern healing environment.

I have already packed up her award, a brand new signed-copy of Jain Malkin's essential new book, "A Visual Reference for Evidence-Based Design," a $200 value.

Picking the winner was difficult. There were many excellent entries. In fact, the entries were so good that I decided to give awards to two other contestants. The two runners up (Jeffrey Yentz and Angela Ahrens) will each be getting a new copy of "Healthcare Spaces No 4."

Thanks to all who entered the contest!

RELIGIOUS ART OFFERS PAIN RELIEF TO BELIEVERS

New research suggests that when believers view religious art, they experience less pain.

Practicing Catholics receiving electrical shocks while viewing an image of the Virgin Mary perceived them to be less painful than shocks delivered while looking at a non-religious picture. In contrast, professed atheists and agnostics derived no pain relief from viewing the same religious image while getting uncomfortably zapped on the hand.

The research was done by Katja Wiech of the University of Oxford in England. Bruce Bower wrote an article describing the research in the October 11 issue of Science News.

I wonder about the implications of this research on art selection in hospitals. If patients have strong religious beliefs, should an attempt be made to change the art in their surroundings to offer images that trigger religious feelings?

Thanks to Dr. Upali Nanda for pointing this out to me.

WORLD PERSPECTIVE

HEALTHCARE ART AROUND THE GLOBE – NORWAY

We live in a global economy, and it may be helpful to understand how those in other countries deal with healthcare art. One way the United States is unique in the world is that we are the only developed country not to offer universal healthcare.

I've been wondering about what effect this change might have on healthcare design in general, and art in particular. If some government agency is in control, won't that mean the end to the art budget as we know it? Not necessarily, if our experience is anything like what they have in Norway. Knut Bergsland, architect and senior advisor at SINTEF Health Research, sent me an email from Trondheim in Norway:

> There is probably less money involved in building hospitals in Norway than in the U.S. because of our public financing methods. As a general rule, however, 0.9 percent of total building cost in hospital projects is supposed to go to art. An approach that might differ from American healthcare: We have artotheques in some of our hospitals. Patients can select pieces of art (mainly paintings, silkscreen and other types of prints, photographic art) for their stay.

Wow! Can you imagine if almost 1 percent of the healthcare construction budget went to art? What a huge boost that would be. I love the idea of artotheques, where patients can choose their own art. Does anyone know of hospitals that offer this in the United States?

IS HEALTHCARE ART NEEDED IN THE THIRD WORLD?

In 1978, I worked as a physician overseas. I worked in Third World medical clinics in Papua, New Guinea, and Kenya. Having seen the abject poverty and chaos, I would argue that you must first cover the basics, and view art as a luxury that comes later.

Should we try to provide art on the walls for a child lying in a hospital bed in the highlands of Papua, New Guinea? A third of his body was burned from falling into the open pit fire in the family's thatched hut. As the physician caring for him, I was trying to find basic antibiotics to fight the infection that ultimately took his life. We did not even have clean sheets for his bed.

Elaine Poggi is a photographer and president of The Foundation for Photo/Art in Hospitals. The mission of the foundation is to place large, framed photographs of nature and beautiful places from around the world in hospitals to give comfort and hope to patients and their families, visitors, and caregivers.

Recently the foundation has provided art for clinics in Haiti, Malawi, and Kenya.

I would argue that until you cover the basics, you are wasting efforts providing art. You would get much more "bang for your buck" by providing immunizations and basic public health measures, such as clean water and proper sewage treatment. Having simple antibiotics might have saved that child's life.

I believe providing money for art is misguided in Third World countries. That money is better spent on donations to the World Health Organization or the Bill & Melinda Gates Foundation.

COMMENTS

Thanks, Henry, for mentioning The Foundation for Photo/Art in Hospitals and our mission to place nature photographs in hospitals around the world.

"Is healthcare art needed in the Third World?" Your answer is that first the basics must be covered—that art is a luxury that comes later.

I propose another question: Is it right that thousands and thousands of dollars are spent on art in some hospitals around the world, while other hospitals do not even have the basics?

"I would argue that the money spent on fine art in hospitals in developed countries would have been better spent on donations to the World Health Organization or the Bill & Melinda Gates Foundation to provide the basic care to patients in hospitals in the Third World countries..."

Unfortunately, we do not live in a perfect world, and the way most of us spend our money will probably not bring equality and basic healthcare to all people.

However, each of us can use our particular talents to make healthcare better for people in all countries.

Evidence-based research in hospital design suggests that appropriate nature art can, indeed, improve the health of patients. I am a photographer. This is where my talent lies. I am doing my best to use my talent to help others. I believe my photos are appropriate for patients in hospitals in all parts of the world. The Foundation for Photo/Art in Hospitals gets a lot of "bang for your buck" because we are able to produce a large, framed, beautiful photo for a minimal cost, primarily because I donate my time and all my photos to the foundation. We then donate the framed photos to healthcare facilities in Third World countries, as well as facilities in other countries that lack funding for art. The feedback that I receive from healthcare facilities, particularly the facilities in Third World countries, encourages me to continue...

> Whether it be the proud mothers of newborns, malnourished children, patients of all ages recuperating from accidents or being treated for AIDS and/or tuberculosis, I know that viewing these photos cannot but help lift their spirits and give them a few moments away from their pain and suffering. If that is the

case, then they will have been provided a good dose of 'medicine' that even the best trained doctor would not be able to provide. *—Debbie Berquist Jules, Chief Operating Officer, Hospital Albert Schweitzer, Deschapelles, Haiti*

Through viewing these pictures, a new window to life is opened for our patients, which gives them greater appreciation for the beauty and variety found in nature and the world. Thank you for assisting us in caring for the needs of the entire patient—mind, body, and spirit. *—Kikuyu Hospital, Kenya, Africa*

Thank you a thousand times for putting Malawi on the map through this ministry of Healing Photo Art. You have blessed my family and my country in amazing ways. May God prosper this ministry that speaks silently but so powerfully of the magnificent power of the Creator of all the nature that exists. *—Haswell Beni, Malawi*

It is highly appreciable the cause you have taken which will really provide great peace, calmness, soothing, and a healing atmosphere to patients and their respected relatives. We will be happy to be part of this great mission you have taken for the uplifting of patients. We wish you the best luck in this mission ahead. *—Chahat Khan and Dr. Shafi Wani, Republic of the Maldives*

Posted by: Elaine Poggi | April 10, 2007 at 03:23 AM

Thanks for your thoughts! You ask: "Is it right that thousands and thousands of dollars are spent on art in some hospitals around the world, while other hospitals do not even have the basics?"

This is very difficult to approach. It is painful to acknowledge the vast disparity in wealth and services between our world and the Third World.

I like your argument that "each of us can use our particular talents to make healthcare better for people in all countries." Essentially, you are discussing volunteer work, and that is very different than regular work. You are volunteering your work and I applaud that.

With regular work there are budgets and limited resources. If one is faced with limited resources, I would still argue that the basics of public health be covered before we think about art.
Posted by: Henry Domke | April 11, 2007 at 06:46 AM

While I agree that money can be used for important medical services and medications, many of these poor, less fortunate souls can look at such wonderful photos as their escape to a life less harsh. After all, these photos provide a glimpse of places they will never experience. I can personally attest to the healing value of photo art in hospitals and clinics—my own father was touched by the beauty of the world he saw in these photos during a recent medical procedure. It is an escape and allows the patient to put himself in another place as visual healing. I have photos like these in my home and office, and they are a welcome "oasis" to me when I need them most. I feel this is a small and inexpensive addition to any Third World medical facility and is a special gift to patients AND medical personnel alike. Art such as this is not a luxury, but a necessity—examine the research or, better yet, survey the patients who look at these photos compared to bare, sterile walls.
Posted by: Tina Ahearn RN, Barnes-Jewish in St Louis, MO USA | April 16, 2007 at 08:57 PM

I agree (and research supports) your idea that nature photos can provide a welcome "oasis" during harsh medical encounters. Perhaps they can even enhance healing. My argument against it is simply one of priorities. Certainly you agree that it is more important to have safe drinking water than to have nature art on the walls? In Third World countries the budget does not allow for much. They must pick carefully how to spend their money.

However, if someone like Elaine Poggi is generous and will volunteer to donate art, then that is a wonderful gift.
Posted by: Henry Domke | April 17, 2007 at 06:22 AM

I have been blown away by the art posted in this blog and am grateful to Henry for creating this forum.

I would like to address the previous question, "Is healthcare art needed in the Third World?"

Native cultures have healing symbols in their own cultures. Some of these symbols come out in weavings, paintings, stories, and a variety of other ways, please consider that. Blessings, Marty Gradolf
Posted by: Martha Gradolf | April 19, 2007 at 09:57 PM

Interesting question! Could healing symbols be used as art in Third World countries? Would they be superior to pictures of nature?

If anyone has experience with this please add a comment. This sounds like the job for a medical anthropologist.
Posted by: Henry Domke | April 25, 2007 at 07:28 AM

INTERNATIONAL ACADEMY FOR DESIGN AND HEALTH

It is easy today to get ideas from experts around the globe. Trying to see how those in other countries view the same problems we face can help us find better solutions. For those involved in healthcare design, there is an organization dedicated to this idea: The International Academy for Design and Health.

I asked director general Dr. Alan Dilani to answer a few questions.

Tell me about your organization.
The International Academy for Design and Health is a nonprofit organization with an inter-disciplinary network dedicated to stimulate research and the application of research concerning the interaction between design, health, and culture.

Our belief: Health is a process consisting of biological and psychosocial factors, life style, emotions, and experiences.

Our goal: Strengthen health processes through a better understanding of the factors influencing health and life quality by design.

How is the International Academy for Design and Health different from The Center for Health Design?
There is a lot of similarity. The difference is that the academy is internationally oriented, while The Center for Health Design is only American!

Has the International Academy for Design and Health ever sponsored or presented research on the impact of art on healthcare?

We have not sponsored such studies, but we do a lot of research and present the results in our congress and publish in the book of 'Design and Health.' We have several papers on art, and soon more than 100 articles that we have published during the last 10 years will be available.

Is the term "evidence-based design" widely used at the International Academy for Design and Health?

We use the term of evidence-based design, and we try to develop this definition further by research and application of case studies.

Nature photography is increasingly popular in North American hospitals. Is that also true in Sweden?

Sweden is well known for its nature, and we use very often the art that is related to nature to attract our mind in order to start a mental process.

How is art paid for in Swedish hospitals?

In Sweden, art is almost 1 percent of the cost of construction in hospitals and other public institutions like elderly, schools, etc.

COMMENTS

The main aim of this site is to strengthen health processes through a better understanding of the factors influencing health and life quality by design. So we can also find some important points of health.
Posted by: Raj | July 31, 2007 at 04:31 AM

With all due respect to Mr. Dilani, he is incorrect in stating that The Center for Health Design's work only focuses on America. While that is the genesis for our work, our resources are used by design and healthcare professionals all over the world. In addition, we are currently talking to healthcare organizations in Australia and Europe about joining our Pebble Project research initiative. There has always been international representation at our conferences.
Posted by: Sara Marberry | July 31, 2007 at 01:33 PM

Please see our publication: http://www.designandhealth.com/sidor/ publication.htm. Look at the articles and see the speakers that have been selected for our congress and compare with them!

Posted by: Alan Dilani | July 31, 2007 at 05:39 PM

Sara and Alan, thank you much for your comments!

Would you each agree that the key difference between The Center for Health Design and the International Academy for Design and Health is that the IADH has a much stronger emphasis on having an international perspective?

If you look at the board of directors of each organization, the CHD has 14 members on its board of directors and each is from the United States. The IADH has six members on its executive board, each from a different country (Italy, Sweden, Germany, United States, Korea, and Canada).

On the other hand, as Sara said, the CHD has been expanding its scope to be more international. In addition to the Pebble Projects for other countries, it has always strongly featured healthcare design leaders at their yearly conference. For example, at the healthcare design conference in 05, the keynote speaker was Knut Bergsland from Norway.

Alan, perhaps you overstated the case when you said "The Center for Health Design is only American!"

Posted by: hdomke | July 31, 2007 at 05:51 PM

CHINESE PAINTERS DEVASTATED BY RECESSION

Buying oil paintings from China can be a great way to save money on a hospital art project. But apparently the painters have been hit by the economic crisis, just like we have.

I had no idea that many of the oil paintings that hang in hotel rooms and starter homes across America are actually produced in just one Chinese village, Dafen, north of Hong Kong. And I had no idea that Dafen's artist colony—the world's leading center for mass-produced artwork and knockoffs of masterpieces—had been devastated by the bursting U.S. housing bubble.

This information is from the December 21 New York Times editorial by Thomas Friedman. It is titled, "China to the Rescue? Not!"

AUSTRALIA'S LARGEST HOSPITAL ART COLLECTION

The Royal Perth Hospital art collection is the largest hospital collection in Australia.

They aren't joking when they say large; there are more than 1,000 paintings, drawings, and wall-based sculptural works on display.

This collection was started in 1954 by art collector Sir Claude Hotchin. He "believed that the public should have the opportunity to engage with art in their everyday lives—outside usual art galleries." He was quite an important benefactor to the arts in western Australia. According to the post on Wikipedia:

> Between 1948 and 1977, Hotchin donated an estimated 2,000 original paintings to galleries, hospitals, and shire councils throughout the state in an effort to 'stimulate art appreciation.'

I emailed the hospital to ask a few questions.

Who is in charge of the collection?
My name is Lance Hyde, and I am the curator of artworks at Royal Perth Hospital, Perth, Western Australia.

Who funds the purchase of new art? Who selects that art? What is the process?
There is no specific policy regarding indigenous or other ethnic works in the collection. WA artists are all treated ethically; however, we follow direction from Indigenous leaders, the artist, and community representatives, in the case of regional or spiritual concerns. (This is usually in the mortuary area of the hospital, or in trauma and emergency areas.)

Is evidence-based art considered?
The hospital doesn't have a policy in regard to evidence-based art. However, we do follow professional healthcare recommendations in

reference to scenes relating to death and passing, other images that may cause offense, disorientation, or may be too similar to blood.

Anything else you would like to say about the collection?

The collection is more than 50 years old and has 1,016 works. Much of the collection was bequeathed to the hospital by Sir Claude Hotchin in 1972; however, much of this collection, around 500 works, was already in the hospital. Sir Claude Hotchin believed that the everyday man needed to see art in his daily environment, and that this would be beneficial to the patients, visitors, and the staff.

How many pieces in the collection are from artists that are not Australian?

I would say that at present 97 percent of the collection is sourced in Australia and represents mainly Western Australian and Australian cultural heritage. The collection follows a policy of acquiring works that have a local cultural significance, or represents how an artist's work has been evolving over time, say one work from each decade or from an exhibition of importance.

The collection is similar to a state art gallery, with a bonus in that we can collect the smaller, less-known artists and the new up-and-coming works in the year of their manufacture. Through auctions and dealers, we can also fill the gaps in the collection, and have a very comprehensive body of work.

The hospital sometimes receives donations or gifts that are made to the hospital wards. In this case, the artwork is not in the collection, it is classed as ward furniture; however, it may be from Africa or South America.

HOSPITAL ART IN VENEZUELA

A frequent contributor to this blog, photographer Elaine Poggi, sent me a picture and email from Venezuela. The picture shows a child in an infectious disease ward. They are using their cell phone to take a picture of the art provided by The Foundation for Photo/Art in Hospitals.

Here is an email to Poggi from Jessica, her contact in Venezuela:

I just came back from one of the hospitals. JM de Los Rios. We hung five of the pictures you sent. It was an incredible experience. We put them in the infectology ward, where they have most of HIV patients.

You have no idea the effect your pictures have caused; both hospital staff and patients were incredible happy! I have to translate for you some of the things they said, but they had a patient—she is a 16-year-old mother who has a 3-month-old baby, both HIV+—the condition of the baby is critical. The girls are very poor. They've been in the hospital for three weeks, and when we hung the pictures, she went out, smiled, and said to us: 'Finally, something that gives me a reason to smile in this place.' It was amazing.

Going today to the hospital and looking at those people's faces, smiling, having nice comments on the photos, taking pictures of them—it was a wonderful experience.

For information about how to make a donation to The Foundation for Photo/Art in Hospitals, go to their website at www.healing-photoart.org.

DUBAI HOSPITAL WINS INTERIOR DESIGN AWARD

I keep hearing that Dubai is the hottest place on earth for new construction. So I wasn't surprised this morning when I was drinking my coffee and surfing the web to see the headlines, "Moorfields Eye Hospital Dubai Wins Commercial Interior Design Award."

The surge in hospital building in the United States is dwarfed by the construction boom in the Middle East. According to a recent article in the International Medical Travel Journal:

Countries from United Arab Emirates to Qatar and Saudi Arabia are pushing to dramatically expand and improve their healthcare systems. The region's ruling families are recruiting brand-name U.S. medical institutions and private investors, with plans over the next 20 years to more than quadruple the estimated $12 billion spent annually on healthcare. Dubai Healthcare City is the best known . . .

It will be interesting to see what kind of art is selected to go in these new healthcare facilities. These are Muslim countries and, based on the Koran, Islamic art does not show animals or humans. Traditional Islamic art is shown through floral, non-object-related art and calligraphy. Will these new high-end Western style hospitals and clinics stay with tradition, or follow a more modern approach to the art on their walls?

INDIAN HOSPITALS – HOW DO THEY USE ART?

I asked Shounak Ray, a healthcare consultant living in India, to offer some observations on the use of healthcare art in India.

My first thoughts were about the hospitals that cater to the predominant multitude. I thought of the rather plain, sometimes derelict and always over-utilized public hospitals dotted across the terrain, and all I could think of are these interesting ceramic tiles that adorn certain key locations of circulation spaces, such as corridors, staircase corners, and even across long stretches of external walls.

The tiles are almost always white and are interspersed with sticker images of Hindu Gods or Goddesses, the Islamic Ka'aba, a Sikh temple image or various other religious insignia. The objective is primarily to dissuade the visiting public from spitting betel (or 'paan') juice that could leave indelible stain on the walls.

For the external walls, it prevents hordes from urinating or defecating on them, thus maintaining a general enhanced level of hygiene in the surroundings. They look interesting and make the walls easy to maintain as well.

This, at any rate, would be an example of art used for convenience, and though not squarely aimed to provide healing, they aid in maintaining practical hygiene and perhaps, function as objects of divine solace to the visitors in their abject anxiety.

Some private hospitals fare a little better on this count. I do not know if there is any specific professional help solicited by them to procure the art for their edifices and spaces. What I have seen in my past commissions as project manager is that the promoter of the project gets together an eclectic mix of artwork/paintings/hangings (hardly ever any sculpture, come to think of it!) from their artist buddies.

Having said that, I must hasten to add that the trend has bettered with time. This has not been so much owing to the fact that hospital promoters/owners/architects have commissioned for professional help to get this done, but more for the fact that these very people have been exposed to the benefits of the use of art in healthcare spaces abroad, and they have thus tried to ape the trend and, as such, have had serendipitous success at times.

BYARD ART FOR HEALTH

Byard Art for Health describes itself as "a new way of sourcing fantastic contemporary visual art for hospitals and other healthcare facilities working exclusively within the NHS."

The National Health Service is the publicly funded healthcare system of England; it provides healthcare to English citizens at no cost.

Byard Art for Health offers easy one-stop shopping for art. If you don't have the money to buy the art, you can rent it. If you don't see what you like, they can help you commission the art.

They describe the contemporary art they feature as "visually accessible," and some that is "more challenging." Most of the prints, sketches, and paintings featured on their gallery page were abstract, and a couple were impressionistic. Among the 26 artists represented, none showed any straight photography, and only one (John Cheall) had a highly realistic landscape.

Nowhere did I see any reference to evidence-based design, which is currently the rage on this side of the Atlantic. Much of the art they feature would not fit evidence-based art guidelines.

ART DUBAI—CONTEMPORARY ART FAIR IN THE MIDDLE EAST

Dubai has a LOT of new buildings, and those buildings are going to need a lot of art. To answer this need, Art Dubai was created in 2007. This year's show, which just ended, has doubled in size to include more than 70 international galleries. The art on display is not traditional Middle Eastern art. Instead, it is art that would fit at any of the many international art fairs.

Artreview.com has a more in-depth post about Art Dubai on their blog.

Dubai is booming. Its population doubled in the last 10 years to 1.2 million people. Its gross domestic product was $37 billion in 2005. Amazingly, only 6 percent of the GDP was oil and gas related.

It has some of the most intense commercial construction activity of any place on earth. Much of this construction is highly innovative and being done by top designers from all over the world.

To learn more about Art Dubai, the official website is www.art-dubai.ae.

ART IN ITALIAN HOSPITALS (PART 1)

Elaine Poggi has kindly agreed to do some investigative reporting on the art scene in Italian hospitals. This is her first report.

From my experience, I find that the private clinics in Florence have much more art displayed than the public hospitals. Most of them are villas that have been converted into healthcare facilities, and they all have a hotel-like atmosphere. Much of the art is abstract and some of it is religious. There doesn't seem to be any plan or theme to the placement of art.

I've spent considerable time in Villa Cherubini—surgery on my broken ankle; five months later, surgery on my husband's broken ankle; plus, my in-laws both passed away there. The villa dates back to the 1850s, and in 1928 was converted into a Catholic healthcare facility. Since 1991, it has been a private clinic run by friends of mine. I have always been fascinated by the Arlecchino figure that greets visitors in the entrance. It is curious, colorful and catches your attention. Behind the sculpture is a very abstract painting, and just up the stairway is another piece showing the Madonna and Child. There you have it all as you enter this facility—humor, abstraction, and religion—all in the form of art.

Poggi was born in America, but has lived in Italy for decades. She founded and heads The Foundation for Photo/Art in Hospitals, a nonprofit, publicly supported organization dedicated to placing comforting nature art in hospital worldwide. She is also a fine photographer and frequent contributor to this blog.

ART IN ITALIAN HOSPITALS (PART 2)

Elaine Poggi continues her investigative reporting on the art scene in Italian hospitals.

The following are my thoughts on the old public hospitals in Italy. I'll write another article on our new public hospitals later . . .

Many of the public hospitals in Italy date back hundreds of years. The oldest hospital in Europe is Santa Maria Nuova, just a few blocks from my office in Florence. Parts of this hospital date back to the late 1200s. Thus, it is easy to imagine that the structures of the facilities may not be in great shape. Most, if not all, of these old hospitals do not have funding for art in their budgets because funding is poured into the maintenance of the structures.

When I enter these hospitals, sometimes it is difficult for me to breathe because of the depressing atmosphere, the dirty and bare walls, the uncomfortable and mismatched furniture, the patients waiting for hours in tiny waiting rooms. It is just awful . . .

Fortunately, in the last few years there are signs of improvement. Sometimes the doctors or nurses, at their own expense, will put up posters or photographs on the walls of their area. Through The Foundation for Photo/Art in Hospitals, I have donated hundreds of nature photos to many hospitals all over Italy to add some color. I would say that the need for art to brighten these old facilities is urgent.

WELSH HOSPITALS TO USE ART TO HELP PATIENTS

It looks like the movement to use art as part of the healing process is not confined to North America. I ran across an article on the use of art in hospitals in Wales. Interestingly, the article was from an Indian website called Medindia.com. The article is titled, "Art in Hospitals to Enhance Patient Care."

The artist has to be part of the design team for new hospitals. This is to ensure that patients' morale is boosted by the work of art.

The radical plan, outlined in a draft strategy, is one of a number of plans to increase the role the arts play in boosting people's health.

Peter Tyndall, chief executive of the Arts Council of Wales, said art can have a beneficial impact on patients. He said, "For a relatively small proportion of the overall cost, it can make a huge difference to the quality of environment that is created. The design life of a new hospital is about 60 years; if you invest at the start of the build, taken over the life of the hospital, it is a small cost.

"Research has demonstrated that an artistic environment can lessen the requirement for pain-killing drugs in a hospital setting."

Art has always been associated with a positive effect on both health and well-being—research by the Chelsea and Westminster Hospital found that live music helped reduce anxiety in patients receiving chemotherapy; visual arts and live music also helps reduce anxiety and depression in patients during the preoperative process. The arts are also playing an increasing role in people's general well-being and day-to-day health.

BOOKS AND JOURNALS

"THE GUILD SOURCEBOOK OF ARCHITECTURAL AND INTERIOR ART, VOLUME 23"

Yesterday the UPS truck showed up with a box containing the latest edition of "The Guild Sourcebook of Architectural and Interior Art, Volume 23."

The book is a rich visual reference for those seeking art for health-care. This year the book features 11 artists that are "Moving toward Green." I'm happy to say that they asked me to be one of those artists (see page 250).

To learn more about "The Guild Sourcebooks," I interviewed Jenna Brandt in May 2007.

What is unique about your service?

The Guild represents more than 1,200 top artists working in media from glass, sculpture, and prints to furniture, lighting, and jewelry. The Guild sourcebooks offer a professional and comprehensive marketing package to artists while working to connect the design trade with professional artists and their work. Our sourcebooks have resulted in thousands of new art commissions for public and private spaces.

How are artists selected for inclusion?

Artists either contact The Guild or The Guild contacts artists about participation in The Guild sourcebooks. Once an artist has made the decision to participate, a space reservation is made. All artists are then juried into the sourcebooks based both on quality of artwork and photography. Our jury is comprised of design and art professionals, as well as The Guild's design, production, marketing, and trade professional relations staff members.

Do you have a sense of what percentage of your readers are involved with healthcare design?

We have a large number of interior designers, architects, and art consultants who work in healthcare design. We find that these professionals are interested in both of our books — 'The Guild Sourcebook of Architectural & Interior Art' for public areas, both indoor and out; and 'The Guild Sourcebook of Residential Art' for smaller-scale work for patient rooms and other private areas.

How many copies are printed?

10,000 copies are distributed annually to a select list of North American architects, interior designers, art consultants, public art administrators, landscape architects, liturgical consultants, and other design professionals. This publication showcases site-specific architectural and interior artworks for public, corporate, healthcare, hospitality, and liturgical spaces.

'The Guild Sourcebook of Architectural & Interior Art,' published each fall since 1985.

How many artists are represented?

On average, about 250 artists are represented in each publication.

Is there a website that shows the artists?

All current sourcebook artists are on-line. You can view both 'The Guild Sourcebook of Architectural & Interior Art' and 'The Guild Sourcebook of Residential Art' page-for-page in Guild's Custom Design Center at www.guild.com/cdc.

For artists who might be interested in receiving more information, you can contact us at 1-800-930-1856.

WHAT KIND OF PICTURES I'LL BE MAKING THIS YEAR AND WHY

Healthcare design leader Jain Malkin offered me some clear advice on what kind of art is ideal for patient rooms. We were talking between lectures at the Healthcare Design conference in Chicago. I scribbled some notes on a small notecard:

- Landscapes during warmer seasons when vegetation is verdant and flowers are visible
- Calm water, not stormy conditions
- Images showing a visual depth or openness in the immediate foreground
- Flowers that appear healthy and fresh, not wilted or dead

I kept asking more questions, and finally she told me to read chapter 7 in "Putting Patients First" by Frampton, Gilpin and Charmel, 2003. She was right. This chapter offers a concise summary of how evidence-based design applies to art in healthcare.

> The decisive criterion for healthcare art is whether it improves patient outcomes, not whether it receives praise from art critics and artists or approaches museum standards for quality.

I suggest that all those involved in healthcare art read these 30 pages. I will be consciously changing the images I create this year because of it.

Jain Malkin is president of Jain Malkin Inc. in San Diego and serves on The Center for Health Design board of directors. Malkin is also the author of "Medical and Dental Space Planning," which is the definitive reference on healthcare interior architecture.

THE BRAIN: THE CORE OF EVIDENCE-BASED DESIGN

"Architecture and the Brain: A New Knowledge Base from Neuroscience" by John P. Eberhard is an exciting new book that explains what is at the core of evidence-based design: our brain. It is in the brain where we experience the emotions that are reactions to the

built environment. The website that accompanies this book is www.
architecture-mind.com.

I asked Eberhard to share some thoughts about what neuroscience has to do with art, and specifically art in healthcare settings:

> A patient in a healthcare setting who is looking at a photograph or painting uses the processes of comparing the image before them with their personal record of past images. When they find a suitable comparison they may register pleasure with the new image or displeasure depending on their past experiences and the nature of the new image. These responses carry with them emotions that the patient will express as feelings. We can observe these feelings, but the emotions that underlie the feelings are not able to be observed, nor are they consciously available to the patient.

John P. Eberhard, FAIA, is founder of the Academy of Neuroscience for Architecture. The academy was the recipient of the AIA's 2003 Latrobe Fellowship, a $100,000 research grant.

"BETTER BUILDING DESIGN" BY SARA MARBERRY

Last weekend I finished reading a new book by Sara Marberry, executive vice president of The Center for Health Design. The book is titled, "Improving Healthcare with Better Building Design."

Pros:
- Clearly and concisely presents the argument for evidence-based design
- Easy to read
- I don't know of a better place to find this much useful and up-to-date information

Cons:
- Expensive ($68 seems like a lot for a thin paperback)
- Boring black and white cover
- No photographic illustrations (hey, I'm a visual person)

Target audience: Healthcare executives who are considering a new healthcare facility.

Goal: Practical suggestions on how and why to improve the quality of healthcare with better building design.

Background: This slender paperback book (it is only 185 pages) summarizes concisely the key ideas that have come out of the work at The Center for Health Design. A different healthcare or design expert writes each of the nine chapters.

How useful would this be to those involved in healthcare art? Not very.

It does provide a broad look at the market you are dealing with. However, it only offers a few paragraphs on the use of art. A better place to learn about what evidence-based design can teach us about art in healthcare is chapter 7 in "Putting Patients First" by Susan Frampton.

BUY THIS BOOK: "CONTEMPORARY WORLD INTERIORS"

I strongly suggest that you buy "Contemporary World Interiors" despite the fact that it is huge. It is not easy to hold in your lap at 512 pages and 7.4 pounds, but you will be rewarded for the time you spend with it.

This is not a book about healthcare art; in fact, it shows very little conventional art (sculpture, paintings, or photographs). In this book, the interiors are the art.

It does, however, have an entire chapter (45 pages) devoted to therapeutic spaces; that covers hospitals, clinics, and spas.

This is not just a drop-dead gorgeous coffee table book filled with wonderful pictures. Author Susan Yelavich has written a thoughtful survey of the current state of international interior design. When I say international, I'm not just talking North America and Europe. She covers the globe, including projects from China, Russia, Brazil, Israel, South Korea, and even Botswana. Yelavich writes well, and the text and pictures are sure to push the boundaries of what you think interiors should be.

I was struck by the fact that I've seen very few of the places in the book. It made the interiors I experience seem very drab. It makes me want to get out and experience these places. Clearly this is cutting-edge design. It fits the pattern set by the publisher of the book, Phaidon Press. (FYI—I liked the series of books by Phaidon Press on contemporary artists so much that I ordered the entire 46-book series. Whenever I am hitting a creative dry spot, I pick one of the books at random to read and it inspires me.)

BEAUTY UNDER ATTACK

A recent conversation with photographer and artist Deanna Dikeman has made me go back to the books to try to understand the place of beauty in art today. I have to admit, I find the whole issue a bit puzzling. How could it be that the words "art" and "beauty" would not be linked? Neal David Benezra wrote a book on this topic in 1999 titled, "Regarding Beauty: A View of the Late Twentieth Century."

In the preface, he writes:

> While ascribing beauty to art may seem natural and appropriate, in recent decades beauty and contemporary art have been considered virtually incongruous. In an art world increasingly focused on global issues and social concerns, artists and critics alike have questioned beauty's efficacy and relevance for contemporary culture. Suggesting frivolity, the machinations of the art market, and a lack of seriousness and social purpose, beauty has indeed come under severe attack. The assault on beauty by the contemporary art world has left a confused and baffled art-viewing public uncertain about one of the very cornerstones of Western art and culture, namely, the pursuit of beauty.

Peter Schjeldahl is my favorite art critic. In 1999, he wrote in The New Yorker:

We don't depend on new art to provide us with beauty, which is just as well. Don't blame the artists for this. Ever since art lost the patronage of clerics and aristocrats who required beauty to justify their authority, it has been stuck with serving the scarcely voluptuous agendas of bureaucratic and educational institutions, novelty-craving commerce, political ideologies, and, in the best instances, rawly ambitious and audacious individuals. . . .

Beauty harmonizes consciousness from top to bottom. It is as organically vital as digestion. Beauty is—or ought to be—no big deal, though the lack of it is. Without regular events of beauty, we live estranged from all existence, including our own.

"HEALTHCARE SPACES NO. 3"

One of the gifts for me under the Christmas tree this year was the book, "Healthcare Spaces No. 3," by Roger Yee.

A key part of healthcare design is its appearance. To really understand what is happening I want pictures—lots of high quality full-color photographs. That's what this coffee-table book is all about. I have Yee's "Healthcare Spaces No. 2," so I knew what to expect in this book. I'm not disappointed. These are high-end, high-dollar projects; something to dream about.

The book is organized alphabetically according to 40 design firms, ranging from Anderson Mikos Architects Ltd. to Wilmot/Sanz Inc. Each project has a few short paragraphs and four to seven high-quality pictures, one usually full-page. Most of the pictures were professionally photographed, but many were computer generated. They are so well done that sometimes it is hard to tell if the image was real!

Even though the book does not focus specifically on art in healthcare, many of the pictures show installed art, which ranges from prints to paintings, sculptures, murals and mobiles. Many of the projects showed the use of plants inside and out.

Yee, a prolific author, graduated from the Yale School of Architecture. He has 23 books currently listed on Amazon, including

"Healthcare Spaces No. 4," which is due out in February 2008.

One mildly annoying thing about this $60 book (only $37.80 on Amazon.com) is that it has a few advertisements, like a magazine. Also, I wish the book had a more global perspective; all of the 150 projects featured are from the United States.

THE ART COLLECTION OF DETROIT RECEIVING HOSPITAL

During lunch yesterday, Sarah Colby, program coordinator for Arts + Healthcare at Barnes-Jewish Hospital Foundation in St. Louis, told me about a wonderful art program at a hospital in Michigan that started in 1968. She even brought along a book about the program, which I paged through. I was impressed with the diversity and quality of the work. The collection ranges widely from folk art to free-standing contemporary sculptures to the tasteful use of recycled tile in a drinking fountain.

For more information on the collection, visit www.drhuhc. org/art.

SHOULD THE GOVERNMENT REGULATE ART?

In March I attended the symposium "The Importance and Value of Art in Healthcare" at the Museum of Modern Art in New York. One of the best speakers was Bill Ivey. Since he was such a good speaker, I figured he would be a good writer, so I ordered his new book, "Arts, Inc.: How Greed and Neglect Have Destroyed Our Cultural Rights."

Conclusion: I disagree with his argument that the government needs to do more to protect the arts.

The crux of his argument is that art needs the advocacy of government to protect us from the greed of big business. I just can't accept that. The digital era is starting to liberate artists from being dependent on big business.

Most artists these days have websites to reach the public directly. They don't need the government for that.

Artists now have the tools to produce their own finished product without having to rely on a big studio. Musicians can record and distribute their own CDs. Digital tools (cameras, printers, high-speed Internet) have allowed me to run a thriving art business in a remote rural area.

I would argue that the arts in America are stronger now than they have ever been. One reason for that is that our government, for the most part, stays out of the way. If we want to ensure that the arts in America continue to thrive, we just need to be sure the government does nothing other than assure artistic freedom.

Bill Ivey was the chairman of the National Endowment for the Arts from 1998 through 2001, was director of the Country Music Foundation from 1971 to 1998, and was twice elected chairman of the National Academy of Recording Arts and Sciences. He presently serves as founding director of the Curb Center for Art, Enterprise, and Public Policy at Vanderbilt University.

"DESIGN DETAILS FOR HEALTH"

How long does a book remain useful after it is published? Most books, especially reference books, don't last. "Design Details for Health" by Cynthia Leibrock, however, seems fresh, even though it has been a decade since it first came out. As architect Wayne Ruga said, "...this book is a reference standard with timeless value."

Granted, nowhere in the book will you see the term "evidence-based design," because that phrase was not in widespread use a decade ago. But the book is packed with useful ideas that would be of real value to interior designers working on healthcare projects.

In 300 pages, Leibrock covers the entire field of healthcare in depth. Long-term care, subacute care, ambulatory care, and inpatient hospitals each gets a section with several chapters. The writing is clear and very practical. Frequent references to "real-world" projects are given with pictures and floor plans.

Summary: Great comprehensive reference book for interior designers working in healthcare

Pros:
- Practical advice that is easy to access
- A well constructed book with high-quality paper

Cons:
- Very little about the use of art in healthcare
- Lots of floor plans and useful photographs, but only a few are in color

Leibrock is the principal/founder of Easy Access to Health (www. AgingBeautifully.org) in Ft. Collins, Colo., a firm that offers consulting services in patient-centered design, planning for independent living. She was selected as a Changemaker in 2002 by The Center for Health Design.

"HEALTHCARE SPACES NO. 4"

"Healthcare Spaces No. 4," by Roger Yee, was just published; mine came last week. I received a complimentary copy since I'm advertising in it this year. It looks to be up to the high standards of the previous editions.

In case you are not familiar with the "Healthcare Spaces" books, they are richly illustrated coffee table books that showcase the most exciting healthcare buildings in North America. Looking at the 800 high-quality images is inspiring and lets you know what the top firms are creating.

Observations: The color photographs are luscious, but it's hard to tell which are computer generated and which are real. Blurred people seem to be the norm in both.

I was surprised (and pleased) by how forcefully Yee presented the serious problems we face in America with soaring healthcare costs and mediocre results, especially when compared to other developed countries. The provocative opening sentence to the book is: "Being an American may not be automatically bad for your health."

The use of art in healthcare is not discussed, but you can see a wide range of 2D and 3D art in many installation shots. Some of the art (especially for kids) is pretty wild (see pages 27, 45, 90–93, 123, and 235).

There are no healing gardens featured, but most of the buildings show attractive conventional landscaping.

Most people who get this book will probably not read the text, but they should. Yee wrote a fine essay titled, "Is Design a Cure?" on page 252.

"Healthcare Spaces No. 4" is available on Amazon.com for $37.50.

CHECK OUT HEALTH ENVIRONMENTS RESEARCH & DESIGN JOURNAL

When we registered for the Healthcare Design conference, they gave us a bag of "stuff." Most of it I threw out, but one thing did catch my eye, a journal I had never seen before: HERD.

This was the first issue that is a joint venture between The Center for Health Design and Vendome. It's an academic journal, and many who are involved in the use of art in healthcare may find it too dry; there are no pictures and no ads. However, I am excited about reading it and plan to subscribe ($229/year).

When I did a survey yesterday about how much solid research supports design decisions in healthcare, it became clear that there is a lot to learn. This journal promises to be the key place to learn about evidence you can trust to allow design to truly be evidence-based.

You can find more information at www.herdjournal.com.

HOSPITAL DEVELOPMENT MAGAZINE

Hospital Development is a British magazine that has been covering healthcare design since 1969. Their website says they cover a wide range of healthcare design topics, including infection control, healing design, sustainability, furniture and furnishings, doors and windows, security, lighting, building systems, energy management, HVAC, floors, bathrooms, and interior design.

Healthcare art is also covered. I found an article in the May 2007 issue titled, "Making the Case." It discusses what needs to be done to communicate the economic, as well as the clinical, value of the arts in health. This is particularly challenging in the UK since healthcare (and healthcare art) is funded primarily by the government.

One very appealing thing about this magazine is that an on-line version of it is provided for free and at high enough resolution that it can easily be read on-line.

The magazine is focused primarily on what is happening in the United Kingdom, but I did see a few articles covering other countries, including France and Dubai.

NEW JOURNAL: WORLD HEALTH DESIGN

World Health Design is a new journal published by The International Academy for Design and Health. To learn more about it, I interviewed Marc Sansom, the marketing and communications director, by email. Sansom is based in Essex, England.

Is there a plan to have articles about the use of art in healthcare?

Art in healthcare is a hugely important topic, and often underestimated by decision-makers in respect of its contribution to the health and wellbeing of patients, staff and families in the healthcare environment. We will be providing coverage of this key topic in WHD, but also hope to work with partners on supplemental reports and publishing projects to promote the research and practice being done in the field.

Who is the intended audience?

Design and health is a global knowledge community with an international interdisciplinary network of health planners, architects, designers, engineers, health managers, clinicians, nurses, health scientists, psychologists, constructors, and industrialists working in research and practice in government, academia, and business. The audience of WHD reflects the make-up of this network.

If someone wanted to subscribe, how do they sign up? What does it cost?

Subscription offers are available for both individuals and teams for one or two years and are a great value for money. To subscribe, download a subscription form from www.designandhealth.com.

How often does it come out?

World Health Design is published four times a year, but we hope to publish bimonthly in 2010.

How many different countries is it being mailed to?

The readership is truly global and coverage is provided across all the major continents of the world in both the developed and developing world.

What is the website for the magazine?

Information on the magazine is available at the website for the International Academy for Design & Health: www.designandhealth.com.

We are, however, also in development of a new, modern and interactive website platform for both World Health Design and the International Academy for Design & Health, which we hope will be launched by the end of September.

RESOURCES: HEALTHCARE DESIGN MAGAZINE

Whenever I ask colleagues, "What is the most useful magazine to learn about art in healthcare?" almost everyone says the same thing: Healthcare Design.

It is easy to understand why it is so popular.

- "Art Corner" is a great column featuring artists working in healthcare.
- The publication has very high-quality images and printing.
- It reaches a broad audience, recently expanding to international coverage.

- Articles are consistently well-written by leading authorities to help you understand trends in the industry.

The fact that it is in partnership with The Center for Health Design is a major plus. It also helps sponsor the most important yearly healthcare design conference every November.

You can subscribe to the magazine for $125 a year.

ART IN AMERICA

Art in America is my favorite magazine for contemporary art, and it has just gotten better. Starting with the December issue, they have a new layout that editor Marcia Vetrocq calls ". . . refreshed, the type is updated, the illustrations more generous." I agree; now it seems closer to the look of a fine art book.

Granted, 95 percent of the art they show would never appear in a hospital, but it is fascinating to see what is going on in the art world. The December issue focuses on contemporary art from Asia. In addition to looking better, they continue to improve their writing. I especially like the pieces by Dave Hickey and Peter Plagens.

One area of weakness is the publication's absence from the web. Vetrocq writes, "A.i.A. acknowledges that it's been less than prompt in taking advantage of all that the web can offer. On the horizon in 2009 is the rollout of our upgraded website."

A one-year subscription to Art in America costs $29.95.

WEBSITES AND BLOGS

RESOURCES: WEBSITES (PART 1)

Where are the best places to find answers about healthcare art? What magazines, conferences, books, people, companies, and websites are people using? Because I'm trying to learn more about healthcare art, I've been trying to find the best resources out there. I thought that might be useful to share.

One of the first people I asked for advice was Nikki Goodemote, an interior designer with Burt Hill Kosar Rittelmann in Pittsburgh. She suggested two websites:

- American Art Resources
- Trade Only Design Library

She warned me that you must have a username and password to enter these sites. That is annoying, but still worth doing because they are very rich sites. Both sites have a huge collection of art that would work in healthcare settings, but only American Art Resources is specifically designed for healthcare. Both sites have powerful search features to let you narrow down your choices.

Trade Only Design Library is primarily an on-line store for designers. American Art Resources is much more than that. They are a full-service art-consulting firm.

COMMENTS

Today I got this question from an artist whom I contacted. They did not want me to post their name: "If I might ask maybe a stupid question, why exactly are you doing this blog?"

Hey, that's not a stupid question. In fact, my family asked me the same question.

From a selfish business perspective, I suppose I hope that if others find the blog of value, then that might have them check out my website and lead to sales.

But also, I am doing it so that I can learn about the business and better understand my clients' needs. If I can understand what their concerns are, then I might be able to do a better job for them.

I did many searches on-line and couldn't find any other websites or blogs exactly along these lines. So I thought: well, if no one else offers this kind of blog, I guess I'll just have to make one up. Then I can share the knowledge with others who might be interested.

Perhaps it could become a forum to discuss controversial issues. For example: Is abstract art wrong in healthcare settings? Is it wrong for people expert in art to select art for healthcare settings? Is the most popular art the best art when people are sick?

Does that make sense?

Posted by: Henry Domke | April 13, 2007 at 10:17 AM

RESOURCES: WEBSITES (PART 2)

My twin sister Beth Worthington is an interior designer who has done a lot of work in healthcare. I asked her to name the websites she finds most useful in her work. This is what she said.

Actually, my most frequently used website is The New York Times. It is my homepage. It keeps me informed on an hourly basis. Being informed helps me in my work. A good interior designer is educated and informed. Being a professional means always learning more about the industry and your clients' needs.

Architectural update—www.ArchNewsNow.com informs me of architectural info from all over the world. I read it daily.

Interior design update—www.interiordesign.net keeps me informed of projects and new products in interior design. I review it weekly.

Ease in finding a new product—www.todl.com. This includes finishes, lighting, interior architectural materials, carpeting, window treatment, furniture, equipment, art, plants, and accessories. These websites are useful in showing me new products. I review them at least once a week. They help keep me informed in the industry. These sites are also great general source for all product info. They are easy to navigate quickly.

Ease in finding the right product—www.specsimple.com is especially good because this site has a wide range of info from healthcare, schools to corporations. I use it once every two weeks.

COMMENTS

Websites are, of course, supplemented with professional journals. I read Healthcare Design magazine monthly for info on healthcare. I'd love to know other websites frequented by designers.

Posted by: Beth Worthington | April 20, 2007 at 03:05 PM

RESOURCES: WEBSITES (PART 3)

I asked Kelly Dubisar, an interior designer at Leo Daly in Omaha, to share websites that she refers to frequently with her work. She agreed with some we have already covered, but added four more:

- The "Specialty Directory" of Healthcare Design magazine (www.healthcaredesignmagazine.com). "Great resource for healthcare related products and design."
- Metropolis Magazine (www.metropolismag.com). "Essential for cutting-edge design and amazing products."
- Tropics North (www.tropicsnorth.com). "Brilliant images for inspiration in healing environments."

- International Interior Design Association (www.iida.org). "Provides tremendous information on industry news, resources, and continuing education for designers and students."

I would like to second her suggestion about the "Specialty Directory" on Healthcare Design's website. It is free, does not require registration, and is very easy to use. I've used it many times and, in fact, I have my business listed there. If you are looking for healthcare art, they have three separate categories that might interest you:

- Art consultants
- Art for medical facilities
- Art, ceiling

PICKING COLORS WITH KULER

Kuler is Adobe Labs' free web application geared toward the design crowd. It is an on-line color scheme creator. Interior designers and hospital facility staff might find this helpful as they are creating new spaces and want to consider what colors would work well together.

It is a web-hosted application, which means you do not have to install it on your computer; it simply runs in an Internet browser, such as Internet Explorer. You can find it at http://kuler.adobe.com.

You can create your own color schemes using the tools provided, and you can see what other people have put together. For example, I typed "hospital" in the search field and it came up with various color swatches.

If you use Adobe's other products (such as Photoshop and Illustrator), it can use the swatches you create or find in Kuler.

NEW BLOG DISCUSSES RESEARCH FOR DESIGNERS

Research Design Connections calls itself "The knowledge tool to create great places." The site is full of useful information and is easy to navigate. It is almost free of advertising (just a few subtle Google ads). I should also mention that there are very few pictures. This means the website is very fast, but for visual people (like me), it makes the experience less rich.

Recently they have started a blog to discuss research of interest to designers. The blog's web address is www.researchdesignconnections. com/blog.

I asked senior editor Sally Augustin a few questions.

When did you start Research Design Connections? Was it print first? Then web and print?
RDC began publication in 2002. Initially, it was printed on paper, then electronically and on paper; now we are an entirely electronic publication.

How do you pick research to feature?
I pick research that I think would be useful to practitioners for inclusion in RDC and on the blog.

Are you trying to be like "Cliffs Notes" to summarize the key nuggets of information so that designers don't have to waste their time reading all day?
I am trying to provide practitioners and interested parties with the information that they need to apply recent scientific research.

Do you rate research for its quality or do you comment on its usefulness?
I include research that can be applied by practitioners and that has been included in peer-reviewed journals or other reputable sources (a research firm with a strong reputation, etc.).

How is the blog different than that? Why have a blog?
The blog was introduced so readers could learn of new information via RDC every day.

Who is your intended audience?
Our intended audience is designers of all types (architects, interior designers, landscape architects, urban planners, industrial designers, etc.), facilities managers, and interested others.

Can people submit articles for you to post?

I would consider articles submitted by others for publication on the blog. Guest experts are recruited for RDC.

The on-line journal requires a subscription, yes? But the blog is free?

The blog is free.

NEW BLOG: CENTER FOR HEALTH DESIGN

I've complained about the lack of other blogs out there dealing with healthcare design. That just changed. The Center for Health Design just started a blog and it looks great. You can find it at www.healthdesign.org/blog.

Overall, this looks like it will evolve into a wonderful blog, and I encourage everyone involved with the use of art in healthcare to subscribe to it.

Initial observations on the blog:

Positives:
- Authoritative—posts are written by the knowledgeable CHD staff
- Up-to-the-minute information
- Conference news
- It's free and easy to use
- Personalizes the staff at the CHD
- Multiple authors—brings in a greater range of experience

Negatives:
- No images. Design is visual process; why no pictures?
- Multiple authors—this might be confusing; I'm used to following blogs with single authors.
- Not posting every day. I prefer blogs with daily updates. Keeps you coming back.
- Not enough hyperlinks within the posts, e.g., if you do a post on NeoCon, link to it.
- No posts on the use of art in healthcare (yet).
- Some kinks need to be worked out. (The "subscribe" button does

not work, and I was unable to see comments from anyone. Comments are one of the features that make blogs more of a dialogue.)

There are many things to learn about here. For example, on a post on May 17, Sara Marberry reflected on a conference put on by the Center for Health Management Research. I was not even aware of the CHMR, and it was useful to be introduced to it.

ART BLOGS—THE GROWING PRESENCE OF ART WRITING ON-LINE

"In a blog, there's the potential for real dialog with an art audience. Eventually, on-line criticism will bury anything in print—newspapers, magazines, books."—Regina Hackett, quoted in an article by Peter Plagens, "Report from the Blogsphere" in the November 2007 issue of Art in America.

Peter Plagens asked the authors of five different art blogs to participate in a roundtable discussion about how blogging is being used to discuss art today. More specifically, it is about how blogs are affecting art criticism. Art criticism is a written evaluation of visual art that discusses art in the context of aesthetics or other theories.

For many years, contemporary art criticism has been found primarily in two magazines
• Art in America
• Art Forum
Now that use of the Internet is so widespread, the presence of on-line art criticism is starting to assert itself through blogs; that is what this article explores. Here are some of the questions:

• What is the purpose of art blogs?
• How does one make blogs pay?
• What is the relationship between blogs and the print media?
• Are blog posts inevitably shorter than magazine articles?
• Do blogs help correct the geographical bias in print art criticism, i.e., the tendency to think that the most important stuff happens in New York City?

Here are the five blogs the article refers to:

- Art To Go
- PORT
- Modern Art Notes
- artblog
- edward_winkleman

TOP FIVE BLOGS FOR HEALTHCARE ART

"Where are the other blogs on art in healthcare?" I asked six months ago. I'm still not coming up with much. The top five blogs I have selected deal with the edges of healthcare art: evidence-based design, contemporary art, and architecture. Surprisingly, my Google searches did not find much on healthcare interior design or art consultants.

- BLDGBLOG—Photos and commentary about architecture from around the world
- Looking Around—Reflections on art and architecture by Time Magazine's art critic Richard Lacayo
- Modern Art Notes—The Wall Street Journal recently called this "the most influential of all visual-arts blogs"
- The Center for Health Design Blog—A group blog for the staff of The Center for Health Design, which seeks to improve the quality of healthcare through evidence-based building design
- Research Design Connections Blog—A blog to discuss recent research of interest to designers

If you know of any blogs that deal with the use of art in hospitals and medical clinics around the world, please let me know.

NEW SOCIAL NETWORKING SITE FOR THE ART WORLD

Artreview.com is a new social networking site for the art world.

The idea behind social networking is that it focuses on the building of on-line social networks for communities of people who share interests and activities. In the case of Artreview.com, it provides a global forum for discussion, interactivity, and debate about art issues.

This site would be useful for artists, art consultants, interior designers, collectors, and critics.

To access all the features of artreview.com, you have to register. This simply means entering your name and a password. There is no charge. I've signed up and I encourage you to do the same.

Once you have registered you can:

- Post artwork, blogs, videos and audio and have members rate and comment on it.
- Find new artists from around the world.
- Keep up to date with news.
- Access ArtReview magazine archives.
- Find the galleries that represent the artists with ArtFinder.
- Create your own discussion groups and forums.
- Promote yourself and make friends.

Here is how artreview.com describes itself:

Artreview.com is a unique blend of editorial and community content, combining the insight and critical weight of some of today's most important art world voices with the input and opinions of everyday enthusiasts from around the world. Artreview.com lets the art world do the talking.

Artreview.com is based in London. It also produces a monthly magazine, which has the same name.

RIPPLE—NEW ON-LINE SOURCE FOR EVIDENCE-BASED DESIGN

While reading the September issue of Healthcare Design magazine, I learned about a new source of information on evidence-based design: Ripple. You can find it at www.ripple.healthdesign.org.

Debra Levin, president and CEO of The Center for Health Design, called it "...an open-source, searchable database to help you begin to sort through all of the design recommendations and related research out there."

Though in its infancy, you can use it to gather information for decisions, as well as add to its vitality by adding information and joining in on conversations that will soon be available.

When I tested out the website, I was disappointed that a simple search for the word "art" came up with no results. However, the website is just getting started; they are calling it a "beta."

ABOUT HENRY DOMKE FINE ART

We create art to reduce anxiety and provide positive distractions in healthcare settings. The art is based on fresh images of plants, animals, and landscapes. We primarily sell prints on paper and canvas. We offer fast turnaround on large projects, even whole hospitals. We can also work with other vendors to supply wall-sized murals or light boxes for ceilings. We work closely with Skyline Design to offer our images on glass.

Our website serves as the catalog to over 1,600 images: www.henrydomke.com

ACKNOWLEDGMENTS

This book would not have been compiled and written without the inspiration from my good friend Steve Mays, who first planted the seed of an idea (smays.com). Credit also goes to Kim Reiss for editing, and Ana Rogers at Rogers Seidman for her inspiring book cover design and interior layout (rogersseidman.com).